Eating for

Sustained Energy

Liesbet Delport • Gabi Steenkamp

DEDICATION

To all those people with diabetes, who for so long have had to eat "special" foods containing no sugar, and often tasting like cardboard. Thanks to the glycaemic index, they can now enjoy normal, low fat, low GI foods, together with everybody else.

Tafelberg Publishers
Heerengracht 40
Cape Town

Registration no.: 1951/002378/07
First published 2000

20 19 18 17 16 15 14 13 12

Publisher   Anita Pyke
Editor   Elizé Lübbe
Designer   Etienne van Duyker, ALINEA STUDIOS
Food stylist   Engela van Eyssen
Photographer   Willie van Heerden
Production manager   James Hart

Reproduction by   Hirt & Carter, Cape Town
Printed and bound by   Mills Litho, Maitland

ISBN 0 624 03866 1

Acknowledgements

We wish to thank Jan Delport, who managed this project. Without his input, the book would not be what it is today. A great big thank you to our families for their patience in helping us prepare and try out all these dishes, until they were perfect.

We wish to thank the Pick 'n Pay Hotline for the financial assistance given with the cost of the ingredients for the photography of the dishes in the book, as well as the Dry Bean Producers Organization for their support during the compilation of this book. We would also like to thank Binuns of Pretoria for the supply of props, as well as Woolworths for those used on pages 5, 33, 41 and 71.

Last but not least our thanks to the publisher, Dick Wilkins, Anita Pyke and the editor Elizé Lübbe for the faith they had in this project.

We humbly also acknowledge the hand of the Lord in getting this book to fruition.

Contents

AUTHORS' FOREWORD

The Glycaemic Index (GI) is a relatively new nutritional tool that has had such a profoundly positive effect on all our patients' health, that we feel we have to share this knowledge with as many people as possible. Stable blood-glucose levels are very important for everyone and by applying the basics of the glycaemic index, an improved quality of life can be experienced by all.

Developing really tasty dishes using low-GI ingredients was a great challenge and a lot of fun for us. Using Jennie Brand Miller's book, *The GI Factor*, as our starting point, we succeeded, much to the surprise of our most critical food critics – our families.

The aim of this book is to teach those unfamiliar with the GI concept to apply it on a daily basis. Conditions such as high cholesterol, high blood pressure, gout, high triglycerides, diabetes, low blood-sugar and being overweight often originate in the kitchen, and to prevent and treat these conditions or diseases, we need to reconsider the foods we consume and the way they are prepared.

This book was written as a practical guide and is the first of its kind in South Africa. It enjoys the approval of the Heart Foundation of South Africa, the Glycaemic Index Foundation of South Africa (GIFSA), the South African Diabetes Association (SADA), the Association for Dieticians in South Africa (ADSA), The Institute for Sports Nutrition International (TISNI), the Department of Health, Directorate Food Control, and Associate Professor Jennie Brand Miller from the University of Sydney, Australia, who is also one of the authors of *The GI Factor*.

For more information on the Glycaemic Index, insulin metabolism, the symptoms and prevention of diabetes, Jack Spratt, etc, visit the website of the Glycaemic Index Foundation of South Africa at: www.gifoundation.com or e-mail Gabi Steenkamp at: gabist@mweb.co.za or Elizabeth Delport at: dellas@mweb.co.za.

We sincerely hope you will enjoy the recipes as much as we enjoyed developing them!

Liesbet Delport (Registered Dietician)
and
Gabi Steenkamp (Registered Dietician)

WHAT OTHERS HAVE TO SAY ABOUT
EATING FOR SUSTAINED ENERGY

THE HEART FOUNDATION OF SOUTH AFRICA recommends this book as a healthy, normal way of eating for the whole family and nation. Eating meals from this book on a daily basis will definitely keep cholesterol levels low, the heart healthy and may even prevent coronary heart disease, which is the leading cause of death in our nation.

THE SOUTH AFRICAN DIABETES ASSOCIATION (SADA) gives its full approval of this recipe book as all the recipes give excellent blood-glucose control. This is your opportunity to eat normal food, since sugar need no longer be totally excluded from the diet, provided the meals are low in fat and have a low GI. All the recipes in this recipe book are low in fat, have a low GI and are thus suitable for all diabetics. It is also useful for the prevention of diabetes, of which the whole population is at risk.

LIESBET KOORNHOF, Registered Dietician and President of the Assocation for Dieticians in South Africa (ADSA) comments as follows: 'Congratulations on the development of a very practical new recipe book! The GI is a concept very useful in compiling diets for individuals who experience problems with glucose and insulin metabolism, such as diabetics, the overweight, hypertensives and those with raised blood-lipid levels. This book will help dieticians and their clients achieve success with the practical implementation of dietary instructions which sound easy, but cause grey hairs when it comes to the preparation of appetizing, wholesome meals and snacks.'

DR PAULA VOLSCHENK, Registered Dietician, UK (she is an accredited UK sports dietician but practises in South Africa) and managing director of The Institute for Sports Nutrition International (TISNI) says: 'Individuals wishing to lose weight and sportsmen and sportswomen who have to maintain a high level of endurance, are often faced with hypoglycaemia or low blood-sugar. This can often lead to the overweight person giving up the diet or the sportsmen performing less than optimally. Blood-sugar peaks and the sometimes subsequent low blood-glucose levels are a very big problem for some people. These low-GI and low-fat recipes will help to stabilise blood-sugar levels without the fear of weight gain, when eaten in conjunction with an overall low-fat eating plan. Congratulations to the authors on some interesting and tasty recipes. Many people will be able to improve their overall productivity and performance with *Eating for Sustained Energy*.'

JENNIE BRAND MILLER PhD, Associate Professor in Human Nutrition, University of Sydney, Australia and author of *The GI Factor* and *The Glucose Revolution* says the following: 'The glycaemic index of foods is now regarded all around the world as a scientifically valid way of expressing differences in the blood-sugar raising potential of foods. It has turned many of the old ideas upside down – sugar is not the villain we thought it to be! The highest nutrition body in the world (FAO/WHO) has recommended that everyone should eat a high carbohydrate diet, based on low-glycaemic index foods. How this is done, will depend on your lifestyle and culture. Elizabeth Delport and Gabi Steenkamp are to be congratulated on *Eating for Sustained Energy* which provides delicious low-glycaemic index meals plus useful tips on putting the glycaemic index into practice.'

FOREWORD

For many years diabetics have not only been traumatised, first of all by their diagnosis, but more so by the traditional diabetic dietary guidelines that are consequently prescribed, particularly the 'no sugar' requirement. Diabetics often suffer from a guilty conscience when contravening their prescribed diet. They therefore become 'prisoners of a diet' which, under the best of circumstances, is difficult to follow and requires a great deal of sacrifice.

For the past two decades scientists have begun to understand more about the physiological effect of different carbohydrates. The amount and type of carbohydrates are not absolute determinants of blood-sugar levels. What really matters is the rate of digestion and absorption of carbohydrates. Therefore in any attempt to stabilise fluctuating blood-sugar levels, the critical element will be the use of a tool which reflects the body's response to the carbohydrate food, as well as a thorough understanding of all the factors that may have an influence, whether they be negative or positive ones.

The Glycaemic Index (GI) of foods has proven to be an accurate and successful tool in educating people about achieving and maintaining an even blood-sugar level. Although the Glycaemic Index is easy to use in making better food choices, most people are still at a loss when it comes to implementing the recommended dietary guidelines in their daily routine. Using this recipe book takes away all effort in this regard. In addition, the valuable tips and extra information provided for each recipe add extra value to the publication, making it even more useful and practical for all health-conscious people.

The added information regarding the fat, fibre and sodium content of foods broadens the usefulness, not only to diabetics but to persons suffering from coronary heart disease, the hypoglycaemic, sportspeople and slimmers as well.

Conditions for claims regarding the Glycaemic Index value of carbohydrate-rich foods have been included in the Proposed New Draft Food Labelling Regulations. Consumers can therefore be assured that the GI concept is reliable, and that it is a very practical way of ensuring effective blood-sugar control.

Antoinette Booyzen
Registered Dietician of the Department of Health, Directorate Food Control.

INTRODUCTION

Everybody is in search of sustained energy, yet one hears people complain every day of always feeling tired, having no energy and of chronic fatigue. We believe that the answer to this problem lies in preparing and consuming the dishes in this book. Eating a low-fat diet and learning how to use the Glycaemic Index (GI), can give one an endless supply of energy. It will no longer be necessary to resort to all sorts of other aids, such as caffeine or tonics to pep up, and alcohol or cigarettes to relax.

Carbohydrate is the body's source of fuel and, if you consume the right type at the proper time, you should have sustained energy, instead of feeling hyped up at some times and under the carpet at other times. Eating the low-fat, low-GI way will keep blood-glucose levels even, resulting in feeling great all the time.

In the past it was assumed that complex carbohydrates or starches, such as potatoes, mealie meal and bread, were digested and absorbed slowly, resulting in only slight rises in blood-glucose levels. Simple sugars, on the other hand, were believed to be digested and absorbed quickly, producing a large and rapid rise in blood glucose. We now know that these assumptions were incorrect, and that the general public, as well as diabetics, no longer need to avoid sugar, provided they use it correctly. In fact, we know that table sugar has a slightly more favourable effect on the blood glucose of normal and diabetic individuals than do potatoes, bread and a few other starches, if used alone.

As early as the 1930s scientists challenged the traditionally held view that the metabolic effects of carbohydrates (CHO) can be predicted by classifying them as either 'simple' or 'complex'. In the 1970s researchers such as Otto and Crapo examined the glycaemic impact of a range of foods containing CHO. To standardise the interpretation of glycaemic response data, Jenkins and colleagues of the University of Toronto, Canada, proposed the Glycaemic Index (GI) in 1981.

The Glycaemic Index (GI) is a rating of foods according to their actual effect on blood-glucose levels.

This work disproved the assumption that equivalent amounts of CHO from different foods cause similar glycaemic responses. Furthermore, the researchers concluded that the CHO exchange lists, that have regulated the diets of most diabetics, do not reflect the physiological effect of foods and are therefore no longer sufficient in controlling blood glucose. Scientists proved with research done over the past two decades, that it is not so much the **amount** of carbohydrate, but rather **its rate of digestion and absorption** that determine the physiological response of the body. Research done all over the world since then confirms that the new way of ranking foods according to their actual effect on blood glucose is scientifically more correct.

Consequently the **Glycaemic Index (GI) factor** was developed, whereby **foods are ranked on a scale from 0–100, according to their actual effect on blood-glucose levels.** Glucose is taken as 100, since it causes the greatest and most rapid rise in blood glucose, and all other foods are rated in comparison to glucose. Since the GI is a ranking of foods based on their actual effect on blood-glucose levels, instead of on assumptions, it is much more accurate to use in the regulation of blood-glucose levels.

Using the GI concept, diabetics, low blood-sugar (hypoglycaemia) sufferers, children with Attention-Deficit Hyperactivity Disorder and sportsmen, can all optimize their blood-glucose control. By using the GI concept in combination with low-fat eating, both triglycerides and blood pressure can be lowered and HDL-cholesterol (the 'good' cholesterol) can be increased. For those wanting to lose weight, the increased satiety – and the fact that less insulin (a fat storer) is secreted by a low-GI diet – results in better fat loss.

Even people suffering from cancer, gout and irritable bowel syndrome can benefit from a low-fat diet. Foods with a low GI release glucose slowly and steadily into the bloodstream and do not over-stimulate insulin secretion. High insulin levels are implicated in many of the diseases of our modern lifestyle such as high blood pressure, high cholesterol, high triglycerides, diabetes, hypogly-caemia, obesity and coronary heart disease (CHD).

Apart from havng a **low GI**, all the recipes in this book are also **low in fat**. Fat, especially saturated fat, in the diet is the main dietary cause of heart disease and high cholesterol, being overweight, cancer, high blood pressure and gout. In addition, irritable bowel syndrome is aggravated by a high fat intake and fat is the main dietary promoter of cancer. Fat also causes the body's insulin to work less effectively, leading to diabetes. Furthermore, it was found that it is fat and not really carbohy-drates (starches and sugars) that are fattening. It takes no effort for the body to turn dietary fat into body fat, whereas it takes a lot of effort and energy to convert carbohydrates and protein into body fat. Thin people mostly consume a low-fat diet that is high in carbohydrates and moderate in protein. Fat people eat high-fat diets. Not more than 30% of total energy in our diet should come from fat. In this book we have heeded that recommendation and the fat content of every portion is kept as close to 10 g (or below) as possible (also see page 24).

HOW THE GLYCAEMIC INDEX IS DETERMINED

The blood-glucose response (BGR) to glucose of at least eight to 12 people is measured. This is done on three different occasions in every person and the average value is the BGR of that person. The blood-glucose response to glucose is given the value of 100. Glucose is absorbed quickly from the small intestine and generally causes the greatest and most rapid rise in blood-glucose levels of all foods. Blood-glucose responses of all other carbohydrate foods are also measured by actual blood tests in the same eight to 12 people per food tested and rated in comparison to glucose for that specific person. The average GI of the food for the group is allocated the GI value that can be applied to the general population. One could say that the GI of a food represents its blood-glucose raising potential. Often the GI of a given food is not what one would expect. For example, the GI of brown bread is 80, whereas that of sweetened low-fat fruit yoghurt is only 33. For this reason all carbohydrate-containing foods need to be tested in order to determine their GI. By

guessing the GI of a food, one could be very far out. The GI of over 600 foods have been determined worldwide and more foods are being tested on a weekly basis, overseas as well as in South Africa.

FACTORS THAT INFLUENCE THE GLYCAEMIC INDEX (GI)

Ongoing studies are revealing that the body's responses to food are much more complex than originally appreciated. The following factors have an influence on the digestion and absorption of carbohydrates, and thus on how foods affect blood-glucose levels. In other words, these factors affect the glycaemic index of the food, which is the measure, on a numerical scale, of how carbohydrate-containing foods affect blood-sugar levels.

The degree of starch gelatinisation.

Gelatinisation of starches occurs when the starchy food is exposed to liquid and heat (i.e. cooking). Water binds with starch (e.g. flour) in the presence of heat and gelatinises the flour. When we boil potatoes the heat and water expand the hard compact granules (which make raw potatoes difficult to digest) into swollen granules. Some granules even burst and free the starch molecules. The same happens when we thicken a sauce with flour or cornflour, where the latter is gelatinised by the liquid in the sauce. For this reason many confectionery items that contain sugar have a lower GI than those without. The sugar binds with the water, preventing it from binding with the flour and there-by preventing gelatinisation. The less a starch is gelatinised, the slower it is digested and absorbed. In other words, it will have a lower GI.

Particle size

Intact grains such as whole wheat, whole corn and whole rye have much lower GI values than flours made from the same grains.

Processing

Milling, beating, grinding, mixing, mashing and refining foods raise the GI of that food. That is why we limit the amount of beating, liquidizing or processing in the recipes.

The chemical composition of the starch

Starches, such as rice, can have different types of starch structures which affect their digestibility. Some types of rice such as basmati have a higher amylose content. Amylose is made up of long straight chains of glucose molecules which tend to line up in rows and form compact clumps that are harder to gelatinise and are therefore more difficult to digest. Other rice, with a higher amylopectin content, is much easier to digest and thus has a higher GI. Amylopectin are branched chains of glucose that are larger and more open and are thus much less dense and easier to digest and gelatinise.

Fibre: type and content

Foods containing soluble fibre, like oats and legumes, have a lowering effect on the GI because they delay gastric emptying. Insoluble fibre such as that found in digestive bran, has very little effect on the digestibility of the carbohydrate foods it is found in. Thus foods containing bran do not have a lower GI than those foods without the bran. For example, brown bread and white bread have almost the same GI. But, in very large amounts, bran can lower the GI of the food, as is the case with Hi-Fibre Bran cereal.

Sugar

Sugar may lower the GI of foods that have a very high GI, because the sugar competes with the starch for the liquid for gelatinisation, or the sugar merely has a lower GI than most starches. A good example of this are Rice Krispies as they have a high GI. When they are sugar-coated, the GI is lower, there-fore Strawberry Pops have a lower GI than Rice Krispies! As mentioned above, sugar can also lower the GI of baked goods, since it is inclined to bind with the fluid in baking, preventing it from binding with the flour and thereby preventing gelatinisation.

Protein and fat

The presence of protein and fat in food may lower the GI. However, it is not advisable to eat too much protein or fat. Protein tends to wear out the body's insulin; and fat has the effect of decreasing the effectiveness of insulin. Protein also overtaxes the kidneys and an over-consumption thereof can lead to osteoporosis, arthritis and gout.

Anti nutrients

Phytates, lectins and polyphenols (tannins) normally slow digestion and thereby decrease the GI.

Acidity

The more acid a food, the lower the GI of that food. For example, a green Granny Smith apple will have a lower GI than a yellow Golden Delicious apple.

Cooking, which increases the digestibility of food, would have the effect of raising the GI of that food.

Resistant starch, which develops in some cooked and cooled-down starches/vegetables/fruit, has a slight lowering effect on the GI, especially in the case of mealie meal. Thus cooked cold maize porridge has a lower GI than the hot freshly prepared porridge.

Speed of eating

Studies have shown that blood-glucose levels rise less rapidly when eating more slowly.

HOW TO MAKE THE GLYCAEMIC INDEX WORK FOR YOU

All foods that have a GI of 55 or less are slow-release carbohydrates and are the best choices for inactive people, the overweight, sportsmen one or two hours before exercise, as well as diabetics, hypoglycaemics, persons with high triglycerides and ADHD (Attention-Deficit Hyperactivity Disorder). Slow-release carbohydrates do not result in a sudden and high rise in blood-glucose levels and therefore keep blood-glucose levels even for hours. They are called **low-GI foods**. The low-GI foods are more satisfying and do not cause the release of as much insulin as high-GI foods do. Therefore, low-GI foods also prevent the huge drop in blood-glucose which occurs after the initial rapid rise in blood-glucose levels, which usually happens after eating high-GI foods. High-GI foods elicit a huge insulin response, the body's way of coping with the sudden, sharp rise in blood-glucose. Often this insulin response is too much and blood-glucose levels then rapidly fall to below the starting point, a condition known as hypoglycaemia. This swing from very high to very low blood-glucose levels, due to hyperinsulinism, is now believed to be a contributing factor to most of the lifestyle diseases. These diseases are actually caused by high insulin levels in the blood and could be prevented to a large extent if the general public would consume low-fat, low-GI foods. Researchers regard all foods with a GI of 62 or below as 'safe', even though the theoretical cut-off point for a low-GI food is 55.

Intermediate and high-GI foods, on the other hand, are very useful for sportsmen and sportswomen, during and up to one hour after sport. **Intermediate-GI foods** are those with a GI of between 55 and 70. They are the best choice in the following cases:
● after low-intensity exercise of short duration,
● in the morning after exercising the previous night,
● or directly after moderate activity in diabetics.

Foods with a GI of 70 and higher are called **high-GI foods**. High-GI foods are excellent for the prevention of fatigue and hypoglycaemia in regular sportsmen after doing moderate to high-intensity exercise. High-GI foods should, however, be limited by diabetics under normal circumstances, but are completely safe after **strenuous** exercise lasting two to three hours. High-GI foods are also useful during a **low** blood-glucose 'attack', but it is better to prevent low blood-glucose than to cure it. Anyone wishing to have sustained energy during exercise, should not consume high-GI foods before exercise or when they are inactive, but rather have low-GI foods before exercise and during periods of inactivity.

HEALTHY EATING

Although the Glycaemic Index (GI) classification of carbohydrates, together with a low-fat diet, is the best way to eat to ensure a feeling of wellbeing at all times, this book would be incomplete if we failed to point out the importance of general good nutrition. The most important aspect in this regard is to ensure that you eat breakfast every morning. Breakfast is the most important meal of the day and 'sets the stage', in a manner of speaking, for the rest of the day.

A well-balanced, low-GI, low-fat breakfast has a stabilising effect on blood-glucose, so that by the time lunchtime comes around, you are only just hungry again and have not had a blood-glucose surge or slump all morning. In other words, the body has been able to operate with optimum fuel levels all morning.

A high-GI and/or high-fat breakfast can result in shakiness, fatigue and irritability all day long. This is due to the hyperinsulinism (excess insulin due to the surge in blood-glucose from the high-GI food) that was triggered off first thing in the morning.

Breakfast

We would therefore like to recommend eating a hearty low-fat, low-GI breakfast to keep blood-glucose levels even for the rest of the morning.

Breakfast should consist of mainly low-GI fresh fruit, cereal, porridge and/or bread, depending on your energy requirements. The bulk of your meal should come from low-GI carbohydrates (50–60% of energy).

Add to this a little low-fat protein/dairy (10–20% of the energy) in the form of low-fat milk and/or yoghurt, low-fat cheese, legumes and occasionally an egg (not more than three to four per week) or low-fat fish, chicken or meat.

Ensure that your breakfast is low in fat by using low-fat/fat-free products at all times and only small amounts of added fat in the form of raw, unsalted nuts (except brazil nuts, which are high in saturated fats), mono- or polyunsaturated margarine, peanut butter, avocado or olive/canola oil.

Fruit is the perfect mid-morning snack and should be the preferred choice for slimmers and all who wish to keep their weight in check. Persons who don't have a weight problem can eat any low-fat GI food inbetween, especially if they are not active during the day. (See section on Breakfast Selection for low-GI breakfast ideas, page 28).

The only exception to the low-GI rule is when you have partaken in sport before breakfast or the previous evening. After sport or a workout in the gym, breakfast should consist of high-GI carbohydrates (50–60% of energy) (see GI list, page 26), a little low-fat protein and a little fat as discussed above.

It is important that a high-GI beverage or food be consumed within the first 30–60 minutes after completion of exercise, since the uptake of glucose by the muscles is the most during this time.

Diabetics who train before breakfast should rather take their breakfast carbohydrates from the intermediate GI group (see list at end of Introduction), unless they were active for two to three hours, in which case they can also go for high-GI foods. Non-diabetics who trained the previous evening might get a good blood-glucose response on intermediate-GI carbohydrates for breakfast, but diabetics should rather stick to low-GI carbohydrates the morning after.

Lunch

The modern trend is not to eat lunch. This results in very low blood-glucose levels by supper time. Low blood-glucose leads to feelings of real or even desperate hunger which, in turn, results in overeating. We therefore want to emphasize the importance of eating a low-fat, low-GI lunch, consisting mainly of low-GI carbohydrates, e.g. seedloaf bread, pumpernickel bread, PRO-VITA or any of the low-GI starches (see the GI list on page 25), as well as salad. Add to this a little protein, e.g. lean meat, fish, chicken, low-fat cheese, milk and yoghurt, or legumes. Keep the lunch low in fat by always choosing low-fat products, taking all the visible fat and skin off the meat or chicken before cooking, using fish canned in brine and using only small portions of peanut butter, avocado, 'lite' margarine, low-fat mayonnaise, and olive or canola oil. End off the meal with low-GI fruit or keep it for a snack later on, as explained above.

(For lunch suggestions, see the sections on light meals, salads and soups, pages 40, 46 and 56.)

As explained in the breakfast section, the only exception to the low-GI rule is if you have been active during the course of the morning, or if you did strenuous exercise lasting more than an hour early in the morning. In these cases, intermediate-GI carbohydrates are the better choice for lunch for diabetics, e.g. rye bread, Ryvita or others (see GI list, page 25), and high-GI carbohydrates, e.g. brown or regular whole-wheat bread or similar (see GI list, page 26) for the non-diabetic.

Combining low-GI foods with a high-GI food would result in an intermediate-GI meal. For example, brown bread (high GI) with apricot jam (low GI) and a little pot of low-fat yoghurt (low GI) with a fresh apple (low GI) chopped up into it. Combining the high-GI bread with one or more low-GI foods will bring the GI of the meal down to an intermediate average.

Supper

Eating a low-GI breakfast and lunch, with or without inbetween low-GI, low-fat snacks, will give you sustained energy throughout the day and prevent you from feeling ravenous by supper time. Many women are overweight from nibbling constantly while cooking and many men from raiding the fridge the minute they get home. Eating predominantly low-fat, low-GI food (it need not be much) every three hours results in glucose being released slowly and steadily into the bloodstream without causing a major secretion of insulin. The only exception to the rule again is activity, in which case higher-GI foods are needed. Activity actually has the effect of letting the body use the high-GI food (that is eaten after exercise) as if it were a low-GI food.

Insulin is a hormone that encourages fat storage, so by keeping insulin levels even and low one can actually lose weight more easily, in spite of eating six to seven times per day. Low insulin levels can also protect against lifestyle diseases, e.g. being overweight, diabetes, high cholesterol, high triglycerides and high blood pressure, since all these are caused and maintained by high levels of insulin in the blood (hyperinsulinism). Remember that high insulin levels are in response to high glucose levels in the blood, and low-GI carbohydrates prevent high blood-glucose levels.

The bulk of your supper should once again be low-GI carbohydrates, in the form of vegetables and starch. Approximately two thirds of your plate should be filled with low-GI vegetables and starch (see GI list, page 25) and only one third with protein coming from lean meat, fish or chicken, or beans, peas, lentils or texturised vegetable protein. Vegetarians can use low-fat milk, yoghurt, cheese, legumes or nuts as protein, but should remember that nuts are 50% fat and the intake thereof should therefore be limited. (See Main Meals and Snacks and Light Meals, pages 56 and 62–105 for ideas.)

The only people who should be eating large portions of potatoes, mash, rice, samp, mealierice, pasta made from flour and other high-GI starches for supper, are those who were active during the course of the afternoon (non-diabetics). Diabetics need to have been active for two to three hours if they wish to eat large amounts of high-GI starches.

If non-diabetics who were not active during the day eat high-GI carbohydrates for supper, they could get a reactive low blood-glucose a few hours later or during the night. If diabetics eat high-GI starches for supper, they may find that their blood-glucose will rise above 10 mmol/ℓ about one hour after supper and that their fasting blood-glucose is higher the next morning, i.e. over 7 mmol/ℓ, both of which are undesirable. Eating protein with higher-GI carbohydrates will lower the effect of the carbohydrates on the blood-glucose, but not as effectively as when higher-GI carbohydrates are eaten together with proteins, which contain carbohydrates and have an overall low GI, e.g. low-fat milk, yoghurt and legumes. This is due to the fact that the body takes the GI of the meal to be the average of the total amount of carbohydrate that is eaten at a particular meal, e.g.

Product	Amount	Amount of available CHO	GI of food	Contribution to GI of meal
Brown bread	2 thin slices	22.1 g	80	51.8
Low-fat milk	250 ml	12.0 g	29,5	10,4
Total		34.1 g		62 GI

If, therefore you want to eat higher-GI carbohydrates and have not been active/active enough, rather have low-fat milk, yoghurt or legumes with your meal instead of meat, fish or chicken.

Fibre

Once again this section would not be complete if we didn't say something about fibre. Most South Africans do not come close to the 30–40 g fibre that is the recommended amount that should be consumed per day. Consequently, people develop high cholesterol and high blood pressure, diabetes (since a lot of the high-fibre foods – though not all – also have a low GI), spastic colon (due to eating too much refined foods and too little high-fibre foods) and cancer, especially colon and breast cancer.

Fibre is the name that is given to a group of plant substances that is present in the cell walls of plants and which give plants their structure and form. Plant products, i.e. starches, fruit and vegetables are the only foods that contain fibre.

Please note that although we need a certain amount of dairy every day in order to get the necessary calcium as well as protein to build our tissues, these foods, e.g. milk, yoghurt, cheese, meat, fish and chicken, contain no fibre. Legumes and nuts are the only protein food sources that also contain fibre, but remember nuts are high in fat!

Fibre moves just about untouched through the alimentary canal until it reaches the colon. There are two types of fibre, i.e. water-soluble fibre which is found in oats, oat bran, barley, legumes, pasta, mealies and certain fruits and vegetables, and fibre that is not water soluble and is found in digestive bran, brown and whole-wheat bread, whole wheat, brown rice, etc.

It was found that high cholesterol and high blood pressure do not only come from eating a diet high in saturated fat, cholesterol and salt (in the case of high blood pressure), but that a low-fibre diet also contributes greatly to these problems. Foods high in soluble fibres, which are listed above, protect specifically against these western diseases, since they bind cholesterol in the alimentary canal, preventing and combating high cholesterol and high blood pressure.

Although not all high-fibre foods have a low blood-glucose raising ability, foods that contain mostly soluble fibre have a low GI. If eaten regularly instead of other high-fat, high-GI foods, they can protect against getting type 2 diabetes, since these foods do not overstimulate insulin secretion. Constant over-stimulation of insulin secretion by eating high-fat, high-GI, low-fibre foods may lead to the depletion of the beta cells of the pancreas responsible for producing insulin.

Constipation and colon cancer can be prevented by a high-fibre diet, since fibre shortens the transit time of food through the alimentary canal, which leads to the formation of a bulkier, soft stool and to harmful carcinogens not staying in contact with the mucus membranes of the colon for too long (carcinogens are substances which can lead to the development of cancer). Fibre also absorbs fluids, which make waste products softer and thicker so that they can be excreted without difficulty. It is also thought that fibre absorbs and excretes certain harmful substances even before they are absorbed by the body.

A low-fat, high-fibre diet decreases high oestrogen levels due to the fact that fibre binds oestrogen, one of the female hormones that can lead to the development of breast cancer, if present in too large amounts. Although all types of fibre play a protective role, wheat fibre and legumes are apparently very effective in decreasing the amount of oestrogen in the body. According to the results of a study that was done in Australia by Dr Baghurst, the intake of 30–40 g fibre per day can reduce the chances of contracting breast cancer by as much as 50%. The regular consumption of cabbage can also reduce the risk of getting breast cancer, since the indoles therein bind excessive oestrogen in women. Do not forget to eat citrus fruit (also a source of fibre) regularly, since the oils therein combat cancer that comes from eating too much smoked and charcoal-grilled meat, fish or chicken. Care should be taken to consume dark green and/or dark yellow fruit and vegetables daily, since they contain beta carotene, one of the anti-oxidants which neutralise free radicals, highly unstable oxygen molecules which damage our body tissues and lead to the development of cancer. These products are also high in fibre.

So, although we include low-fibre foods in the GI list so that you can know which foods are low, intermediate and high GI, we want to encourage you to always rather choose a higher-fibre product that is also low-fat and low-GI, instead of its refined counterpart.

DIABETES MELLITUS

Diagnosis of Diabetes

Diabetes is on the increase at a rate of 11% per annum and there is talk of an epidemic of diabetes. This is mainly due to the high-GI, high-fat diet the general public is consuming, as well as an increasingly sedentary lifestyle, stress and smoking. There are two types of diabetes, i.e. type 1 diabetes (10% of diabetics) and type 2 diabetes (90% of diabetics).

In type I diabetes, the beta cells of the pancreas are unable to produce insulin and the onset is usually sudden. A pre-existing genetic component is usually present, as well as a precipitating factor, e.g. a viral infection, or, in some cases, certain proteins can spark off an immune response. Often it is a trigger factor that is the proverbial last straw in the person becoming a diabetic, e.g. an infection, stress or trauma. These do not, however, cause the diabetes. The classic symptoms of especially type 1 diabetes are chronic thirst, chronic urination, chronic hunger and massive weight loss in spite of consuming large amounts of food and drink. Type I diabetics need to inject insulin every day.

Type 2 diabetes is less easy to diagnose than type 1 and the onset is usually slow. Thirty percent of type 2 diabetics already have complications at the time of diagnosis. Usually these people are overweight, have insulin resistance and already have high cholesterol and/or high triglycerides and high blood pressure by the time they are diagnosed as being diabetic. They often have no or vague symptoms, e.g. chronic infections, chronic fatigue, pain/ cramps/burning sensation in the legs and feet, shortness of breath, etc. Some of these people have a relative insulin deficiency and can be treated with diet and exercise alone, or diet, exercise and tablets. Others have an absolute insulin shortage and need to be treated with diet, exercise and insulin therapy.

Early diagnosis is important, so whether you have any of the above symptoms or not, have your blood-glucose, blood lipids and blood pressure checked regularly. The earlier diabetes is diagnosed and treated, the less the chances are of serious complications, e.g. blindness, kidney failure, amputations, heart attacks or stroke.

Modern treatment of diabetes

As with all new research, the Glycaemic Index (GI) has not been welcomed with open arms by everybody. It has its critics who mostly cling to past assumptions due to fear of change. They unfortunately prefer to believe what they **think** should happen to a person's blood-glucose in response to eating certain foods, rather than facing the facts of what **actually happens** to blood-glucose when carbohydrate-rich foods are eaten. The Glycaemic Index, remember, is a **physiological measure** of the body's response to a particular carbohydrate-rich food.

Research conducted over the past 20 years in Canada, Australia, the UK, Italy, France, Denmark, and South Africa, proves beyond a doubt that many foods that were regarded as 'safe' on the traditional sugar-free diet, actually raise diabetics' blood-glucose levels unacceptably high. Some of the previously regarded 'safe' foods elicit very high blood-glucose increases and should therefore rather be avoided. Many other foods that contain sugar, which diabetics have had to avoid in the past, cause no major fluctuations in their blood-glucose. It therefore does not make sense to forbid these foods for diabetics. By consulting the GI list at the end of the introduction (pages 25–26), you will notice that potatoes have a high GI value, whereas sweetened fruit yoghurt has a low GI value.

Therefore, the new lower-fat, low-GI diet is much more effective in lowering and controlling diabetics' blood-glucose, because it is based on what happens to real people (diabetics and non-diabetics) when they eat real food in real life. Umpteen dieticians across the world have countless examples of how diabetics' insulin and oral medication can be decreased or even discontinued in some cases, when following the low-GI, lower-fat diet. Many of these people had been on a sugar-free diet for many years and could still not get their blood-glucose readings under 10 mmol/ℓ As soon as they go on the lower fat, low-GI diet, their readings go under 10 for the first time in years, **not by avoiding sugar, but by avoiding high-fat, high-GI foods**. It is actually upsetting to dieticians to see that many diabetics who have been following a sugar-free diet for years, are in fact eating a high-fat, high-GI diet. This is especially serious, since diabetics are more prone to heart disease than the general public, and many of these diabetics are overweight and it is impossible to lose weight following a high-fat diet. We now know that it is actually fat that is the most fattening nutrient, and not carbohydrate or sugar, as many believe.

A high-fat diet also results in the insulin working less effectively, which, in turn, can lead to a relative or absolute insulin shortage, hyperinsulinism and consequently insulin resistance. This predisposes a person to several lifestyle diseases (diabetes, heart disease, hypertension and to being overweight). The lower-fat, low-GI diet is also much more 'user-friendly' than the old diabetic diet, because sugar is no longer completely forbidden. Portion control is no longer so important when eating low-GI, low-fat foods, as the increased satiety automatically controls how much is eaten. However, those who are overweight still have to watch their portion sizes. That is why we give the portion sizes at every recipe, so that those who want/need to watch their weight are able to do so by sticking to the recommended portion sizes. Larger portion sizes are, however, also given sometimes for those whose weight is normal or who need to carbo-load.

Please note that ALL the recipes in *Eating for Sustained Energy* are suitable for all diabetics.

Every meal consumed by a diabetic should contain at least one low-GI food. If most of the foods in a meal are low-GI, then intermediate and even small amounts of high-GI foods can be added to the same meal. We applied this principle in many of the recipes in this book.

For maximum lowering of blood-glucose levels, especially if you have a fasting blood-glucose value that is higher than 8 mmol/ℓ and a random blood-glucose that is higher than 10 mmol/ℓ, it is very important to consume mainly low-GI foods at every meal.

HYPOGLYCAEMIA
(Low blood-sugar)

Definition and Symptoms

Hypoglycaemia is a condition in which the sugar level in the blood falls below normal levels (hypo=under, glycaemia=blood-sugar/glucose).

Many people suffer from hypoglycaemia today and not surprisingly so, since most of the foods that are freely available and consumed by the general public, are high in fat and have a high GI value. The most common form of hypoglycaemia occurs after a meal is eaten. This is called reactive hypoglycaemia. High-GI foods, except when eaten during or after exercise, cause most people's blood-glucose to surge upwards within a short period of time, i.e. 30–60 minutes after ingestion. The human body then reacts, or overreacts in the case of a person suffering from hypoglycaemia, by releasing insulin to counteract the threat of a sustained high blood glucose. This causes a rapid fall in blood glucose resulting in the typical stress-like symptoms of low blood sugar, i.e. tremor, heart palpitations, sweating, anxiety, sleepiness, weakness and the very common feeling of chronic fatigue. Hypoglycaemia can also affect mental function and lead to restlessness, irritability, poor concentration, lethargy and drowsiness. These symptoms are noticed very clearly in non-diabetics in GI research done by scientists, especially if high-GI foods are eaten.

Consequences

There seems to be the general opinion that, if one suffers from hypoglycaemia, one should eat a lot of sweets (or, according to modern-day thinking, high-GI foods), since there is a lack of glucose in the blood. This is entirely untrue, since it is actually the high-GI foods that bring on the hypoglycaemia, as explained above. If on top of eating high-GI foods one consumes a lot of fat (which causes the body's insulin to work less effectively), it is only a question of time before impaired glucose tolerance (the forerunner of type 2 diabetes) or type 2 diabetes develops. The reason for this is that the body's insulin gets worn out by a high-GI diet, and the insulin which is left cannot work properly due to the high-fat diet. This can lead to hyperinsulinism (too much insulin in response to the high blood-glucose levels) and consequently insulin resistance. The latter causes the body's cells to shut down, since they do not like being drowned in insulin. Other factors that can contribute to insulin resistance are genetic factors, inactivity, obesity and age. Hyperinsulinism, in turn, can lead to diabetes, hyperlipaemia, hypertension and heart disease. This whole vicious cycle needs to be broken before the body will start functioning properly again.

Treatment

The main aim of the treatment of hypoglycaemia is to prevent sudden large increases in blood-glucose levels. If blood-glucose levels can be prevented from increasing quickly, then excessive amounts of insulin will not be produced and blood-glucose levels will not plunge abnormally low. This should greatly improve the feeling of wellbeing, since big swings in blood-glucose levels are hereby prevented. Irregular eating habits and eating the wrong type of foods are the main causes of hypoglycaemia. Eating low-GI food when not exercising, or one to two hours before exercising, causes a steady release of glucose into the bloodstream, preventing an insulin surge (hyperinsulinism). This is especially true if carbohydrate foods are eaten on their own. Thus the body's insulin is not wasted and, if a low-fat diet is followed and regular exercise is done, the insulin is also able to function as it should. It is now believed that diabetes, insulin resistance and most of the lifestyle diseases mentioned above, can actually be prevented by following a lower-fat, low-GI, low-sodium diet, since this type of diet prevents hyperinsulinism.

Prevention

It is better to prevent hypoglycaemia than to try cure it once present. Follow these simple guidelines to prevent it from occurring:

- Eat regular meals and snacks, preferably every three hours.
- Include low-GI carbohydrates at every meal or snack, since the blood-glucose is sustained by slow-release (low-GI) carbohydrates.
- Avoid eating high-GI carbohydrates on their own. Preferably avoid them altogether (see GI list pages 25–26), but if you have to eat them, always combine them with low-GI carbohydrates or at least some protein. Eating high and low-GI foods together yields an overall intermediate GI as explained under Healthy Eating (page 8).

Sport-induced Hypoglycaemia

This occurs when a person does not eat low-GI food before exercise and either eats nothing or low-GI foods after exercise. In order to prevent this, low-GI carbohydrates should be eaten about an hour before exercise. A high-GI beverage or food is required during excercise lasting more than one hour and within the first 30–60 minutes after exercise. By doing this you will perform and feel a lot better.

CORONARY HEART DISEASE (CHD)

In westernised South Africans, 40% of deaths in the economically active age group (25–64 years), are due to chronic lifestyle diseases such as cancer, hypertension (high blood pressure), diabetes, strokes and coronary heart disease (CHD) In fact CHD is the number one killer in South Africa and many other countries of the world today. The development of CHD is a slow process and starts with fatty deposit build-up on the inner walls of the arteries of the heart and brain. This may lead to narrowing of the arteries (arteriosclerosis) that supply the heart and the brain with oxygen. When the blood cannot get through anymore, the person suffers a heart attack or stroke. Often a part of the heart muscle dies or one section of the body is paralysed (stroke), if the person is lucky enough to survive. The frightening thing is that, as fatty deposits slowly constrict and clog your arteries, you won't necessarily suffer any discomfort or pain, except maybe fatigue and short-ness of breath. Some people experience chest pain (angina), but for many the first warning sign could be a heart attack or stroke.

Risk factors

A number of risk factors contribute to an increased risk of CHD. These are high blood cholesterol, high blood pressure, being overweight, diabetes, smoking, stress, a lack of exercise and a family history of CHD. Heart disease claims the lives of more South Africans than both cancer and car fatalities combined. An increasing number of people have also been found to suffer from high blood triglycerides, which is another type of fat in the blood that predisposes a person to diabetes. To decrease these higher triglyceride levels, a lower-fat, low-GI diet is recommended. This differs from the treatment for high cholesterol levels, where a low-fat, high soluble fibre diet is recommended. High blood cholesterol, high triglycerides, high blood pressure, diabetes, being overweight, gout and cancer are all influenced by the amount of fat, especially saturated fat and 'burnt' fat in our diet. Saturated fat causes the body to produce more LDL-cholesterol, which is the dangerous cholesterol, as it builds up in the arteries, causing the gradual narrowing of the blood vessels. Oxidised LDL-cholesterol is laid down in the arteries most easily and that is why it is important to prevent oxidation of LDL-cholesterol by eating lots of fresh fruit and vegetables. The narrower the blood vessels are, the higher the blood pressure rises, eventually causing thickening of the walls of the heart muscle, which is sometimes irreversible. Saturated fat also causes the body to retain dietary cholesterol, which makes satu-rated fat, instead of dietary cholesterol, as was previ-ously thought, the number one culprit in raising blood cholesterol. It can also lower the good HDL-cholesterol, which is another reason it should be avoided. Fat, especially saturated fat, is also believed to be the main dietary promoter of cancer, as well as the main cause of being overweight. Most of the foods South Africans love to eat are high in saturated fats: fatty meat, dried sausage, biltong, toasted sand-wiches, pies and other confectionery such as cakes, tarts, biscuits, rusks, and croissants, full-cream ice cream, chocolate, rich sauces and desserts. Too much sodium, together with a high-fat diet, large amounts of alcohol, smoking, being overweight and lack of excercise usually cause high blood pressure.

Treatment

It is, however, possible to eat most of these foods, provided they are lower in fat and sodium, and lower in their GI value. This book is full of delicious, normal recipes that are low in total fat, saturated fat, GI and sodium and will not cause fatty deposits to build up on the inner walls of the arteries. It was decided to rather recommend the use of canola or olive oil (which are high in monounsaturated fats) in the recipes, since it was found that large amounts of polyunsaturated fatty acids (PUFAs), especially of plant origin, e.g. polyunsaturated soft tub mar-garine, sunflower oil, sunflower seeds and walnuts, can have adverse health effects. This is due to the fact that the consumption of large amounts of these polyunsaturated fats can give rise to nasty reactive chemicals called free radicals, which are implicated in heart disease, cancer and ageing and can also decrease the more favourable HDL-cholesterol. In addition, heating polyunsaturated fats may produce trans fatty acids which are detrimental to our health, e.g. frying foods in oil, especially re-used oil, found in most takeaway outlets.

Polyunsaturated fats which appear in fatty fish, e.g. pilchards, trout, tuna (in water/brine), sardines and salmon (without the oil), mackerel (in water), etc. seem to be much healthier, since they lower fibrinogen levels in the blood, which slows down the clogging of arteries. We would recommend that fatty fish be eaten one or two times per week.

Monounsaturated fats, which are found in olive oil, canola oil, olives, avocado, peanut butter and raw unsalted nuts (except brazil nuts), decrease bad cholesterol and raise good HDL-cholesterol. HDL-cholesterol is the one that is responsible for the removal of the 'bad' fats from the arteries by transporting them to the liver to be excreted. HDL-cholesterol is increased by exercise, a low-GI diet and using monosaturated fats, oily fish and red wine in moderation.

Fibre, especially soluble fibre, also plays an important role in decreasing the risk of CHD. Soluble fibre binds cholesterol in the alimentary canal, thereby reducing serum cholesterol, especially the bad LDL-cholesterol. Other ways to change your lifestyle and thereby decrease the risk of CHD are:

- get more exercise,
- stop smoking,
- decrease your intake of salt, and
- lose weight/prevent becoming overweight.

ATTENTION-DEFICIT HYPERACTIVITY DISORDER (ADHD)

For years it was believed that ADHD was caused, or at least aggravated, by the consumption of sugar. Sugar was believed to cause hypoglycaemia and it was found recently that hyperactivity and/or ADHD and hypoglycaemia are interrelated. Now that we know that it is rather the high-glycaemic index (GI) foods that cause the hypoglycaemia, we recommend that children with ADHD should rather avoid high-GI foods (such as refined bread, most cereals, cold drinks, energy drinks and sweets that are high in glucose), rather than just avoiding foods that are high in sugar.

Why ADHD and hypoglycaemia are interrelated

Many children with ADHD crave high-GI carbohydrates. All high-GI foods cause a rapid rise in blood-glucose. This causes the pancreas to pour out insulin in an attempt to bring the blood-glucose down to a normal level. In many people and some children who suffer from ADHD, the body pours out too much insulin, causing too much glucose to be drawn out of the blood and the blood-sugar level to fall below normal. The result is a hypoglycaemic attack with irritability, poor sleeping habits and lack of concentration (see Hypoglycaemia, page 13, for other symptoms of hypoglycaemia that are usually caused by eating high-GI foods.) When high-GI foods are eaten for breakfast, a hypoglycaemic attack may occur 1–1½ hours later, which is still before first break and at a time when the brain should still be receiving a steady supply of energy from the food that was eaten 2–3 hours before, as is the case with low-GI foods. If high-GI foods are again eaten at break time (which often happens, since the child usually feels the need to compensate for the tired feeling by eating another high-GI food), the same scenario can repeat itself later in the morning, which is the reason we think these children struggle to concentrate. The brain fuel is constantly undergoing huge swings and this is not conducive to thinking or behaving in a normal manner.

Evidence is starting to emerge that an adverse food reaction may also cause a significant drop in blood-glucose. The person's endocrine (glandular) system overreacts and this may cause a sudden rise and later a drop in blood-glucose. It is hypothesized that by eating certain foods over and over again, the enzymes needed to digest and metabolise the food are overextended, until an allergy to that particular food may develop. When an allergic reaction develops, a chemical called histamine can be produced. Histamine causes the adrenal glands to excrete adrenaline which stimulates the liver to convert stored sugar (glycogen) into blood-glucose. This sudden rise in blood-sugar levels can also cause the pancreas to pour out insulin. The end result is a hypoglycaemic attack. The histamine reaction occurs as an immunologic allergy in which actual antibodies against a food are involved. If a child is therefore allergic to a specific food, it can also cause hypoglycaemia and consequently blood-glucose and mood swings. The fact that allergy to a food affects blood-glucose has been confirmed by GI tests done, and we have observed this phenomenon in some of our patients. Caffeine can also cause hyperactivity initially and hypoglycaemia, with the resultant symptoms later. This is because caffeine also stimulates the adrenal glands to excrete adrenaline, which stimulates the liver to pour glucose into the bloodstream. This sudden rise in blood-sugar levels can once again cause the pancreas to pour out insulin. The end result is a hypoglycaemic attack.

Treatment of ADHD

In light of the above, we recommend that all high-GI foods, caffeine and any food to which a child with ADHD is allergic, should be avoided, due to the fact that all of these foods may induce hypoglycaemia. If low-GI foods are eaten most of the time, but especially for breakfast (since breakfast sets the tone for the rest of the day), the brain receives a steady supply of energy from the food. This is because low-GI foods do not result in a sudden, nor high rise in blood-glucose levels and, consequently, there is no sudden drop in blood-glucose due to the over-secretion of insulin. They keep blood-glucose levels even and enable the child to concentrate better. The emotions are also more stable. Examples of low-GI breakfast foods are oats, wholewheat ProNutro, Hi-Fibre Bran, deciduous fruits and fruit yoghurt, to name but a few (see GI list, page 25). It is also still advisable to keep these children away from flavourants, preservatives, and especially colourants, since the latter was found to inhibit the uptake by the brain of a very important neurotransmitter which is vital for the transmission of messages. Children with ADHD also benefit from additional essential fatty acids and certain vitamins and minerals. For more information, consult a dietician who specialises in the treatment of ADHD.

ALL the recipes in *Eating for Sustained Energy* are suitable for children with ADHD.

WEIGHT MANAGEMENT

Eat low-fat

For some or other unknown reason carbohydrates (CHO) have been labelled as fattening for the last 20 to 30 years. Although research done in the past 10 years has disproved this over and over again, carbohydrates are still struggling to get rid of the 'fattening' label. Carbohydrates have actually been found to stimulate their own metabolism, which means that if you eat more of them, your body will merely burn more of them. This is, however, not the case with fat. Dietary fat has been found to simply slip unchanged into body fat, proving that it does not stimulate its own metabolism. If you eat a lot of a certain type of fat such as that found in chocolates, the fat in your body will look exactly like chocolate fat. If, on the other hand, you eat a lot of cheese, the fat in your body will look exactly like the fat in cheese. Scientists in the UK who put a few people into a room for a week, allowing them to eat low-fat/fat-free carbohydrates to their hearts' content, found that these people only gained a maximum of 1,5 kg. When these same people were put into a room and allowed to eat high-fat foods to their hearts' desire, some of them gained as much as 7 kg! This proves beyond a doubt that in order to lose weight (or rather fat), one needs to cut down on one's intake of visible **and** hidden fats. All the recipes in this book are low in fat, and we also show you in the choice of ingredients and preparation methods how to decrease the fat content of all meals and snacks. Do not, however, avoid fat altogether. One needs a small amount of good fats in the diet in order to get in all the essential fatty acids, owing to their favourable effect on blood lipids, as well as to prevent cravings owing to too strict dieting (see Heart Disease, page 14, and Mass building, page 19, and note the inclusion of small amounts of good fats in the recipes. Also see page 24 for Jack Spratt logos showing different fat percentages and GI values).

Eat regular, small meals

Regular, small, snack-type meals are recommended to lose weight and keep slim. Increased insulin secretion is stimulated when large meals are eaten and insulin plays a role in how we store fat. Better fat loss is achieved when smaller, more regular meals are eaten. This is because small meals only stimulate the secretion of small amounts of insulin.

done in South Africa, as reported in *The GI Factor* by Jennie Brand Miller, et al, it was found that over a period of 12 weeks persons on a slimming diet containing only low-GI carbohydrates lost 2 kg more than their counterparts who were placed on a diet containing only high-GI carbohydrates. The astounding thing was that both groups were given the exact same **amount** of fat, kilojoules, protein, carbohydrates and fibre. The success of the low-GI slimming diet was attributed to the fact that a low-GI diet does not cause a major insulin response, resulting in lower insulin levels **and more even blood-glucose levels**. This, in turn, assists the body in losing body fat, which is prevented by high insulin levels. This is a major breakthrough, since there is a school of thought that believes that people can only slim on a high-protein, low-carbohydrate diet, since carbohydrates are believed to elicit a major insulin response, leading to hyper-insulinism. As explained above, this is not the case with **low-GI** carbohydrates. By limiting high-GI carbohydrates (except after exercise) and empha-sizing low-GI carbohydrates, and consuming the prudent diet (page 8), body fat loss is **optimised**. Low-GI carbohydrates are also more satisfying and the hunger pangs therefore stay away longer on a low-GI diet. On the other hand, high-GI carbo-hydrates usually cause a reactive hypoglycaemia, and thus one is inclined to eat sooner due to low blood-glucose (also see Hypoglycaemia, page 13).

Exercise regularly

Regular exercise increases lean body mass, which in turn increases the metabolism. In contrast to this, body fat has no influence whatsoever on metabolism. If one exercises regularly while slim-ming, it is impossible to lose **lean** body mass and therefore a slowing down of the metabolism is hardly noticed, unless the energy intake is cut down too drastically. Trying to slim without doing regular exercise can lead to muscle loss, especially since the body finds it easier to turn muscle into energy than to burn body fat for energy. This is especially true if the food intake is cut down too drastically. Therefore, in order to lose fat most effectively, don't do anything drastic! Forget about dieting and just eat regular low-fat, low-GI meals (except after exercise) and exercise daily. Your slimming eating plan must be one that can last the rest of your life. Do watch your portion sizes though, since you still won't lose weight if you eat too much (to help you we have included the portion sizes for each recipe). Last, but not least: be patient. It takes time to burn fat!

If small meals are also eaten regularly, the body is never starved and there is therefore no major increase in insulin secretion due to this either, since a person is less inclined to overeat.

Hyperinsulinaema is a major contributor to being overweight, high body-fat levels and an inability to lose weight. In order to get and stay slim, it is therefore of the utmost importance that there should be no major increase in insulin secretion. It is also important not to cut food intake too drastically, since any major cut in food intake, especially to levels below 4200 kJ per day, usually leads to a slowing down of the metabolism.

Eat low-GI foods

Another aspect of weight loss is to keep blood-glucose levels as even as possible. The best way to do this is to use the Glycaemic Index. In a study

SPORTS NUTRITION

The only exception to the low-GI rule applies during and after exercise. Whereas the general public should eat low-GI carbohydrates most of the time if they want to have sustained energy, sportsmen/-women should only eat low-GI carbohydrates (1 g CHO per kg body weight) one to two hours before exercise commences, and resume eating low-GI foods a couple of hours after completing exercise, depending on the duration and intensity of exercise. During exercise, immediately after exercising, and for a few hours after exercising, depending on the duration **and** intensity of exercise, it is best to consume high-GI carbohydrate foods and drinks. For the diabetic sportsman/-woman, intermediate-GI foods are recommended and, **only** if the activity lasted two to three hours, a high-GI food or drink is recommended. It is important to realise that the carbohydrate-storing ability of the body is limited and therefore needs to be replenished regularly by those who partake in sport on a daily basis. It is therefore important to:

Eat/drink low-GI before the event

Low-GI foods and drinks can also be called sustained-release or slow-release foods. They are digested slowly and can therefore still supply energy one to two hours after consumption. If low-GI products are consumed one to two hours before competing, blood-glucose will be maintained at a healthy level for the duration of the activity or sporting event. One gram CHO per kilogram body weight is sufficient.

During the event

Competitions that last for more than 90 minutes require high-GI (intermediate for diabetics) foods and drinks at a rate of 30–60 g CHO per hour, depending on body weight. If the duration of the exercise is less than 90 minutes, the low-GI food/ drink that was taken beforehand should be sufficient to sustain blood-glucose levels at a healthy level, and no carbohydrate intake is necessary during the exercise event.

After the event

It is crucial to consume at least 1 g carbohydrate per kg body weight high-GI carbohydrate food or drink within the first 30 minutes of completing exercise (Intermediate for diabetics, unless competing for two to three hours). Thereafter 1 g CHO/kg body weight should be consumed every two hours after exercise. The reason for this is that the exercised muscles continue to absorb glucose from the bloodstream and this happens at the fastest rate during the first 30–60 minutes **after** exercise. Faster replenishment of glycogen into the fatigued muscle is observed if high-GI foods are taken as soon as possible after cessation of exercise. Severe hypoglycaemia can be prevented by this course of action and one should also be ensured of sustained energy levels. The meal eaten one to two hours after the event should still consist mainly of high-GI carbohydrates (intermediate for diabetics). The next meal can be scaled down to intermediate GI or even low-GI carbohydrates depending on the intensity and duration of the excercise. The meal thereafter should be back at low-GI carbohydrates, provided no activity has taken place again later in the day. For very active persons (those who train two to three hours every morning or an hour every morning and an hour every evening), it might mean having to eat higher GI foods most of the time. If, however, training is scaled down before an event, low-GI carbohydrates should dominate all meals for the best **carbo-loading** effect.

Eating for mass building

Sportsmen (and in fact everyone else, body builders included) should see to it that 50–60% of the total energy of their diet consists of carbohydrate, only 20–30% fat and 12–20% protein. Carbohydrate is the fuel of the muscles and too many sportsmen/-women suffer from chronic fatigue because they eat too little carbohydrate or the wrong GI carbohydrates at the wrong time, and too much protein. This especially holds true for body builders. There is a school of thought that one needs to eat lots of protein in order to build muscle, whereas most body builders will actually consume enough protein if they keep to the recommended 12–20% of energy as protein. The food intake is usually increased due to increased training time, increased muscle mass and consequently metabolism. If protein levels remain at 12–20% of total energy, the actual grams of protein eaten will automatically increase, but so should the grams of carbohydrates and fats. Eating too much protein is expensive, can overtax the kidneys (which is especially dangerous for diabetics), can lead to gout, arthritis and osteoporosis and is really not necessary. Increase in muscle mass happens when the muscle is stimulated at cellular level by lifting weights, and not by consuming extra protein. Many body builders are also inclined to follow diets that are very low in fat, which is mostly unnecessary and very boring. If a diet of less than 30% fat is followed, the intake of essential fatty acids is compromised. Research has found that as sportsmen get fitter, their bodies also become more efficient in using fat as a source of fuel, so that a little extra fat in the diet will not make them fatter, but actually help them to feel more energetic.

Carbo-loading

A legal technique for enhancing sports performance is to eat a high carbohydrate diet consisting of large quantities of bread, potatoes and pasta. This technique is commonly knows as 'carbo-loading' and is followed by athletes during the last three days before competing. Although most will probably perform better after carbo-loading, this technique does not suit everyone. According to Professor Tim Noakes, it is a good idea to try out any dietary changes long before the event you intend taking part in. No one wants to have an upset stomach caused by the high-carbohydrate content of the diet on that day.

Because of this, it is advisable for each sportsman/-woman to experiment with his or her diet before deviating too much from his or her normal eating pattern. Runners should also remember that it is important to drink more water than they normally do during carbo-loading. A light-coloured urine indicates that enough water has been consumed. Although vitamin supplements can also be taken while carbo-loading, one should never take vitamin B-complex tablets during exercise, particularly those containing nicotinic acid, as they impair endurance if taken in high doses. The best sign that a sufficient amount of carbohydrate has been consumed during carbo-loading is an increase in body weight.

To modify your diet when carbo-loading:
- Eat cereals, bread (with honey), fruit and fruit juices for breakfast.
- Use skim milk in place of full-cream milk as it contains no fat.
- Substitute pasta (macaroni, spaghetti, etc.) for meat and eat more potatoes.
- Supplement the diet with 100 g of a high-carbohydrate 'carbo-loading' athletic drink.

A good basic carbo-loading diet could include the following:

FOOD/FLUID	QUANTITY
Orange juice	1 litre
Skim milk	250 ml
Whole-wheat bread	10 slices
Cereals or muesli	50 g
Bananas	3
Apples	2
Potatoes or pasta	200 g

This diet provides approximately 400 g carbohydrate, 45 g protein and 10 g fat, and more than 100% of the recommended daily allowances for thiamine, riboflavin, niacin, vitamin C, calcium, magnesium and iron. It is, in fact, one of the healthiest diets available and could form the basis of a diet eaten all year round. Just remember that, if you are resting while carbo-loading, you should stick to low-GI carbohydrates all the way (see GI list on pages 25–26).

How Sportsmen should use *Eating for Sustained Energy*

To know specifically which high-GI foods to eat during exercise, directly thereafter, and at the next meal, consult the GI table at the end of this introduction. Remember that diabetics who are not exercising for two to three hours or more, should rather choose intermediate GI foods after exercise from the GI table at the end of the introduction. The recipes found in this book are all low GI and suitable for daily consumption and, a few hours after completing an exercise routine, for maximum sustained energy levels.

Those recipes suitable for carbo-loading before a sports event, are clearly marked in bold lettering under the RD note with each recipe. For those sportsmen and sportswomen who need high-GI meals after their sports activity, most of the recipes in this book can have the low-GI carbohydrate substituted with a high-GI carbohydrate which converts the meal into a low-fat, higher-GI meal. For example, instead of the lower-GI basmati rice, or the low-GI rice with lentils, these can be substituted with plain white rice or large potatoes which are both high-GI foods. Pearled barley, pearl wheat (stampkoring), pasta, baby potatoes with skin and sweet potatoes are all low-GI carbohydrates that can be substituted with brown rice, white rice, samp, mealie rice, mealie meal, large potatoes or brown bread. Sportsmen still need to eat a low-fat diet, but high-GI foods are required during and for a few hours after exercise.

NB: If you need a specialized diet plan for a specific condition, with portion sizes and quantities, please consult a registered dietician. For a list of dieticians who specialise in the glycaemic index, go to the webpage of the Glycaemic Index Foundation, at www.gifoundation.com, or contact ADSA per fax on (011) 886-7612.

VEGETARIANS

Last, but not least, this recipe book is also suitable for vegetarians. All the recipes, except the few main courses and quick meals that contain meat, fish and chicken, are suitable for vegetarians. Many of the main courses and quick meals can be turned into vegetarian dishes by simply replacing the meat, fish or chicken with one or two cans of beans. There is also a whole section on main courses that do not contain meat, fish or chicken (see page 74). These recipes teach the inexperienced vegetarian how to incorporate beans and legumes into meals so that they are nutritionally balanced, without the beans dominating the whole meal. Many vegetarians are unsure of how and what to eat. The recipes in this book will help teach the unsure vegetarian how to create vegetarian meals without compromising good nutrition. Please note that not all vegetarian dishes are necessarily low in fat. We had to limit the amount of cheese and other sources of hidden fat to ensure that they are low in fat.

Lacto-ovo vegetarians (vegetarians who do not eat meat, chicken and fish)

It is very important that meat, chicken and fish are replaced with legumes, nuts, eggs or dairy products, i.e. low-fat milk, yoghurt or cheese to ensure sufficient protein, which is essential for building and restoring body tissues. Remember nuts are 50% fat and therefore not the best choice for those with weight problems. Limit brazil nuts, as they are high in saturated fats. Limit eggs to three to four per week.

Lacto Vegetarians

Although dairy products contain protein, it is equally important to replace meat, chicken or fish with legumes or nuts, to ensure sufficient protein, which is essential for building and restoring body tissues. Remember nuts are 50% fat and therefore not the best choice for those with weight problems. Limit brazil nuts, as they are high in saturated fats.

Ovo Vegetarians

To ensure adequate protein, it is important to replace meat, chicken or fish with legumes, nuts or eggs. Remember nuts are 50% fat and therefore not the best choice for those with weight problems. Limit brazil nuts, as they are high in saturated fats. Only three to four eggs per week are recommended. Extra calcium may also be necessary, since dairy products are the main sources of calcium in the diet. Calcium must be consumed on a daily basis to prevent osteoporosis.

Vegan Vegetarians

For those vegetarians who eat no animal products at all, vitamin B12 supplements or injections are required as vitamin B12 is not found in any plant foods. Extra calcium must also be taken to prevent osteoporosis. Plant sources of calcium such as sesame seeds need to be chewed to a fine 'peanut butter' consistency for the body to be able to absorb the calcium. Alternately, the seeds can be ground to a paste such as tahini. Traditional animal protein sources must be replaced with legumes or nuts at every meal. To ensure adequate intakes of good quality proteins, it is advisable to eat starches, vegetables and fruit at the same meal as legumes or nuts.

THE NUTRITIONAL ANALYSIS OF THE RECIPES

The Box: You will notice that there is a highlighted box containing nutritional information with every recipe. All the values are rounded off to the nearest whole number. It contains the following information and reflects the **amounts per serving**:

Glycaemic Index (GI) – this is a calculated value. The value in real life will probably be lower, due to the interaction of the different nutrients with each other.

Fat (g) – This value reflects the total fat content of the serving per person. Although the saturated fat and cholesterol content are not displayed, they are kept low throughout the book. The Jack Spratt markings are a reflection of how well the recipe complies with the low fat and saturated fat requirements as laid out in their specifications and those of the Heart Foundation (see page 24).

Carbohydrate (g) – This value gives the total carbohydrate (CHO) content per serving and includes the carbohydrate present in the dairy, starch, sugars, vegetables and fruit.

Fibre (g) – This is the total amount of fibre per serving, including both soluble and insoluble fibre.

Protein (g) – This represents the total amount of protein per serving.

Kilojoules (kJ) – This is the total amount of kilojoules (energy) per serving.

To convert to calories, simply divide by 4.2.

In each recipe the portions per serving are given. For example: One serving is equivalent to 1 STARCH and 1 PROTEIN.

The **nutritional contents of 1 portion for each food group** is as follows:

Dairy – the analysis for a low-fat dairy portion applies:
530 kJ, 8 g protein, 5 g fat and 12 g carbohydrate. When applicable, the analysis of a fat-free dairy portion was used:
340 kJ, 8 g protein, 0 g fat and 12 g carbohydrate.

Protein – the analysis for a medium-fat protein portion applies:
328 kJ, 7 g protein and 5.5 g fat.

Starch – a starch portion implies the following:
289 kJ, 15 g carbohydrate, 2 g protein and traces of fat.

Fat – a fat portion implies the following:
190 kJ and 5 g fat.

Vegetables – the kilojoules and carbohydrates allocated to a limited vegetable portion are:
119 kJ, 7 g carbohydrates and 2 g protein.
Where the kilojoules that were allocated to the other food group portions in a recipe took up all the kilojoules, we did not count the kilojoules of the limited vegetables, even if the recipe contained a/some limited vegetable(s). Free vegetables contain less than 105 kJ per 100 g vegetables.

Fruit – a fruit portion implies the following:
170 kJ and 10 g carbohydrate.

MEASURING DETAILS

In all the recipes in this book, the following amounts (abbreviations in brackets) were used. We used metric measuring spoons, measuring cups and measuring jugs.

¼ teaspoon (t) = 1.25 ml
½ teaspoon (t) = 2.5 ml
1 teaspoon (t) = 5 ml
1 dessertspoon (D) = 12.5 ml
1 tablespoon (T) = 15 ml

¼ cup = 60 ml
⅓ cup = 80 ml
½ cup = 125 ml
¾ cup = 180 ml
1 cup = 250 ml

JACK SPRATT'S LOWER-FAT CHOICE

Jack Spratt's low-fat choice is a range of marked products that are low in fat, have a GI rating and allow a minimum of sodium. It is available in some restaurants in South Africa as a separate, low-GI, lower-fat menu and the logo also appears on selected products in supermarkets. Please see listed below the logos for the different ratings with the explanations. Each recipe has a Jack Spratt rating.

Jack Spratt Green Plus implies that the product:
- can be eaten freely,
- is very low in total fat, saturated fat and cholesterol (≤ 3 g fat/100 g food),
- has a very low/low GI (0–55), and
- contains little sodium.

Jack Spratt Green implies that the product:
- can be eaten often, i.e. most of the time,
- is low in total fat, saturated fat and cholesterol (≤ 10 g fat/100 g food),
- has a low GI (0–55), and
- has a low sodium content.

Jack Spratt Orange implies that the product:
- should be kept for special treats (Diabetics should preferably reserve it for after moderate exercise),
- is slightly higher in total fat, saturated fat and cholesterol, but still much lower in fat than its regular counterpart (≤ 15 g fat/100 g food),
- has an Intermediate GI (Some of these products could have a low GI, but fall in this group due to the slightly higher fat content) (GI = 0–69), and
- has a low sodium content.

All the recipes in *Eating for Sustained Energy* are low in fat and most of them have a low-GI value. The intermediate-GI values are mainly due to the presence of flour and not sugar. All the recipes, however, have a GI value below 62, which is regarded as 'safe'. All the recipes in this book are endorsed by GIFSA (Glycaemic Index Foundation of South Africa), of which Jack Spratt is the official logo.

The Glycaemic Index list of South African low-fat foods

Foods are in order of GI with the lowest GI at the top
(The GI Value of Glucose = 100)

Low GI (0–55):

Dairy	Cereals	Starches	Fruit	Vegetables	Snacks/ Sugars	Drinks
Low-fat/fat-free milk (plain and flavoured) Low-fat/fat-free yoghurt (plain and sweetened) Low-fat/fat-free custard (sweetened and unsweetened) Low-fat ice cream (sweetened and unsweetened)	Bokomo ProNutro Wholewheat (Original and Apple Bake) Kellogg's Hi-Fibre Bran Cold mealie meal Oat bran Kellogg's All-Bran Flakes with skim milk Bokomo ProNutro Original with low-fat milk Fine Form muesli **Breads** PRO-VITA Seed loaf bread Pumpernickel bread Any other bread with lots of whole kernels, crushed wheat, and oat bran inside	Legumes: all dried and canned beans, peas, lentils, pea dahl, baked beans and tinned pasta Boiled barley Boiled wheat Pasta made from durum wheat (semolina) Sweet potato Mealies/corn Cold samp	All deciduous fruit e.g. apricots, cherries, peaches, plums, pears, apples, etc. All citrus fruit e.g. oranges, naartjies, grape-fruit and lemons. Kiwi and grapes – watch portions!	All those that are not intermediate or high GI.	Fructose – not more than 20 g per day Sugar-free sweets Sugar-free jam Homemade low-fat popcorn	Sugar-free colddrink Juice of low-GI fruits: 1–2 glasses only! Sustagen

Intermediate GI (56–70):

Dairy	Cereals	Starches	Fruit	Vegetables	Snacks/ Sugars	Drinks
None	Kellogg's Strawberry Pops Kellogg's Fruitful Bran Bokomo ProNutro Flakes Tastee Wheat Kellogg's Corn Pops Kellogg's Frosties Kellogg's Choco's Kellogg's All-Bran Flakes Shredded Wheat Mealie meal – reheated or with added corn **Bread** Rye bread Ryvita	Sweetcorn Brown rice with lentils Baby potatoes with skin Couscous Mealie meal porridge – reheated or with added corn Basmati rice	Tropical fruit e.g. banana, mango, sultanas, paw-paw, pineapple and litchis. Dried fruit: Sultanas, dates and raisins. Melons	Beetroot Marogo Spinach	Bakers Home-wheat Digestive biscuits Low-fat biscuits containing oat bran Low-fat bran/fruit muffins/pancakes Low-fat oat bran crumpets Raw honey Jam Sugar Fine Form canned peaches Fine Form apricot jam	Juice of intermediate-GI fruit – 1 glass only! Regular colddrink – cordials and soft drinks

High GI (70 and above):

Dairy	Cereals	Starches	Fruit	Vegetables	Snacks/Sugars	Drinks
None	Mealie meal – refined and coarse Puffed Wheat Maltabella Instant Oats	Potatoes: boiled, mashed, baked and fried Minute noodles Rice, especially sticky rice Samp Mealie rice **Bread** All brown, white and regular whole wheat bread, all bread rolls and anything made with cake flour, bread flour and Nutty wheat flour Rice cakes Snackbread, white and whole-wheat	Watermelon Dried fruit rolls	Carrots and carrot juice Pumpkin, hubbard squash, butternut Parsnips	Sweets – boiled and jelly type Bakers Marie biscuits Commercial honey Glucose Maltose	Game Energade Powerade Lucozade Lucozade-Sport

The GI Research that the Glycemic Index Foundation of South Africa (GIFSA) is currently conducting has been sponsored by Novo Nordisk, National Brands and Bokomo. The GI list is constantly expanding as more products are tested on a regular basis.

GLOSSARY

ADHD (Attention-Deficit Hyperactivity Disorder) Children suffering from ADHD have short attention spans, are easily distracted, are impulsive and display excessive physical activity.

Antioxidant Antioxidants are substances that deactivate free radicals and thus protect the body from their destructive effects. (aging, heart disease, cancer, etc.)

Beta carotene A substance found in red, orange and yellow fruits and vegetables, as well as leafy vegetables. It acts as a potent antioxidant and thus offers protection from cancer and degenerative diseases.

Carbohydrate All carbohydrates are chains of glucose bonded together in different ways and in different chain lengths. Depending on the chemical bonding, carbohydrates are absorbed at different rates. Glucose is the basic unit of energy for the body, and the brain can only use glucose as its fuel source.

Carbo-loading A dietary manipulation with the aim of maximizing muscle glucose stores. Large quantities of slowly absorbed (low-GI) carbohydrates are consumed one or two days prior to the competitive event and proteins and fats are kept to a minimum to encourage the body to store glucose in the muscles. Carbo-loading helps to lessen the effects of fatigue and increase endurance.

Cardio-vascular disease These are the diseases of the heart and/or blood vessels. All cardio vascular diseases are treated with a reduction in dietary fat intakes.

Degenerative disease Diseases of modern lifestyle such as diabetes, obesity, hypertension, cancer, ADHD, ME, cardiovascular diseases, etc.

Diabetes Diabetes is a condition in which the body cannot properly use glucose in the blood because the pancreas is not producing enough insulin (or not producing any insulin at all). Glucose in the blood is derived mainly from dietary carbohydrates. The body may also make glucose from body or dietary protein and/or fats. Insulin enables glucose to move from the blood into the cells where it is used as a fuel source. Without insulin, blood glucose levels go very high and cause various defects in the body. There are two types of diabetes, i.e. type 1 (10% of diabetics) and type 2 (90% of diabetics). People with diabetes have to take daily medication, or inject themselves with insulin at regular intervals.

DRI (Dietary Reference Intake) DRI is based on four nutrient reference values and will replace the RDA (recommended dietary allowance). It includes the RDA, the AI (adequate intake), the UL (tolerable upper level) and EAR (estimated average requirement). They are a better guideline to assessing adequate nutrient intakes.

Essential fatty acids Fatty acids are part of the building blocks of dietary fats. There are two essential fatty acids which must be supplied in the diet, linoleic acid (omega 6), and linolenic acid (omega 3). Linoleic acid is found in plant oils such as borage oil and oil of evening primrose. Linolenic acid is found in certain cold-water fish oils and flax seed oil (linseed oil). Provided the correct nutrients are available, the body can make gamma linoleic acid (GLA) and eicosapentanoic acid (EPA) from linoleic and linolenic acid respectively.

Fats Dietary fats can be saturated, (mainly of animal origin), polyunsaturated, (mainly of plant origin), or monounsaturated (mainly of plant origin). Processed fats such as margarine, contain trans fatty acids which interfere with many metabolic processes. A small amount of fat is essential in the diet and the recommendation to date is an equal amount of each type, not exceeding 30 percent of the total energy of the diet.

Fibre Fibre is that part of plant foods that is not broken down by human digestive enzymes and is excreted in the stool. Fibre absorbs water and thereby keeps the stool soft and thus aids in constipation and diarrhoea. There are two types of fibre; soluble (e.g. oats and legumes) and insoluble (wheat bran). Soluble fibre is effective in lowering the GI of a food, whereas insoluble fibre has no effect on the GI unless it is added in huge amounts. The body needs both types of fibre.

Free radical An unstable, highly reactive molecule of oxygen (e.g. hydroxide) which oxidizes (damages) anything with which it comes into contact. Free radicals are released whenever substances are oxidized (burnt) in the body. All normal metabolic processes require oxidation of substances, therefore it is important that the diet is adequate in antioxidants to neutralize these free radicals.

Gelatinization All starches undergo gelatinization when exposed to water and heat during cooking. Each starch granule becomes hydrated (filled with water like a sponge), and thus the liquid becomes thickened, as in custard or a white sauce.

Glycaemic Index (GI) The Glycaemic Index is a numerical measure from 0 to 100 of how fast and by how much a specific carbohydrate food affects blood sugar levels after ingestion. Carbohydrates with a low GI are digested and absorbed much slower than carbohydrate foods with a high GI. For example, white or brown bread, which has a high GI, is digested and absorbed very quickly, whereas baked beans have a low GI as they are digested and absorbed slowly over a longer period of time (approximately 2 hours). The bread will therefore cause a steep, sharp rise in blood glucose levels, whereas the baked beans will only give a small blood glucose rise over a much longer period of time. For this reason, low-GI foods are referred to as sustained energy release foods.

Gout A painful inflammation of the joints. It is caused when the kidneys fail to excrete excess uric acid of which crystals then accumulate in the joints.

Hyperglycaemia This occurs when there is excessive glucose in the blood.

Hypoglycaemia This occurs when blood glucose levels are too low and there is too little glucose in the blood.

IBS (Irritable Bowel Syndrome) IBS is also known as a spastic colon. It is thought to be due to abnormal function of the small and/or large bowel resulting in cramps, bloating, alternating constipation and diarrhoea.

Insulin Insulin is a hormone produced in the pancreas; it lowers high blood-glucose levels.

Kilojoule (kJ) The term of measurement for the energy values of food. One calorie is equivalent to 4.2 kJ.

Monounsaturated Fats These fats are relatively stable to oxidation and have a beneficial effect on the body's blood lipid profile. Sources include: olives, olive oil, canola oil, avocado and nuts. The recommendation is that one third of total dietary fats should come from monounsaturated sources.

Polyunsaturated Fats (PUFA). PUFAs are relatively unstable fats and are readily oxidized. They are mainly of plant origin and liquid at room temperature, e.g. sunflower oil. Recent research shows that although PUFAs raise the good cholesterol (HDL), they also raise the bad cholesterol (LDL), therefore the recommendation is to use only one third of the total fat intake in the form of PUFAs. Oils should be stored in dark airtight bottles in small amounts to ensure freshness at all times. Heated oils (e.g. potato chips fried in oil) produce trans-fatty acids which interfere with many metabolic processes.

Protein Proteins are complex molecules made up of amino acids needed for growth, repair and maintenance of body structures.

RD (Registered Dietician) A qualified person who specializes in the scientific study and regulation of food intake and preparation.

RDA (Recommended Dietary Allowance) The minimum estimated amount of vitamins and minerals needed by the human body to prevent symptoms of deficiency. To be replaced by the Dietary Reference Intake (DRI).

Saturated fats Saturated fats are mainly of animal origin and are solid at room temperature, e.g. butter and lard. The harder the fat, the more detrimental it is to cardiovascular health.

Vegetarian diet A diet which excludes animal flesh, but includes eggs and milk.

FRUIT AND NUT MUESLI

Makes 500 g (10 x 50 g servings)

225 g (2½ cups) rolled oats
75 g (1½ cups) All-Bran Flakes
75 g (1½ cups) Hi-Fibre Bran cereal
15 g (1½ T) raisins
125 ml (½ cup) sultanas
50 g (4 T) dried peach, pear, apple,
   apricot, chopped
30 g (3 T) mixed nuts, chopped

NUTRIENTS PER SERVING

Glycaemic index 58 ● Fat 4 g
Carbohydrate 28 g ● Fibre 7 g
Protein 5 g ● kJ 736

ONE 50 g SERVING is equivalent to
1½ STARCH and 1 FAT

1 Mix all the ingredients together.
2 Store in an airtight container.
3 Serve with 250 ml low-fat milk.

DIETICIAN'S NOTE:

● When eaten with milk, the GI of the meal is slightly lowered to below 55.
● This muesli is suitable for **carbo-loading** as it has a high long-acting carbohydrate content with not too much fat or protein.
● For **spastic colon sufferers**, remember to omit the raisins and sultanas, and to chop the nuts very finely. (Simply add more of the chopped fruit to make up for the raisins.)
● **Jack Spratt Green** only applies if the muesli is eaten with 250 ml low-fat milk, otherwise it will be **Jack Spratt Orange**.

BRAN AND OAT LOAF

Cuts into 18 slices

10 ml (2 t) instant yeast
400 ml warm water
15 ml (1 T) sugar
500 ml (2 cups) oats
625 ml (2½ cups) Nutty Wheat flour, sifted
250 ml (1 cup) oat bran, pressed down
250 ml (1 cup) Hi Fibre bran cereal
2.5 ml (½ t) salt
1 apple, grated DO NOT LEAVE OUT
30 ml (2 T) canola or olive oil

NUTRIENTS PER SLICE

Glycaemic index 60 ● Fat 4 g
Carbohydrate 26 g ● Fibre 5 g
Protein 5 g ● kJ 668

One SLICE is equivalent to 2 STARCH

1 Place the instant yeast in a cup with 50 ml of the warm water and 5 ml of the sugar. Stir to dissolve all the yeast and set aside, so the yeast can be activated.
2 Place all the dry ingredients and the grated apple in a large bowl and mix well, but not for too long.
3 Make two wells in the dry ingredients and pour half the water into each well.
4 To one well add the oil and, once you have checked that the yeast is active (foaming), pour the yeast into the other well of water.
5 Mix well, but not for too long, with a wooden spoon – this will be difficult as it forms a very stiff mixture.
6 Spoon the stiff dough into a greased loaf tin.
7 Sprinkle with oats and then use your hands to flatten the bread and spread the oats evenly.
8 Leave in a warm spot to prove for 30 minutes.
9 Bake at 180 °C for 60 minutes, or until the bread starts to come away from the edge of the loaf pan.

This makes a very dense, moist and heavy bread that is excellent with soup or used for coffee shop type open sandwiches.
It is not suitable for packed lunch type sandwiches.
Sliced, this bread freezes well.

DIETICIAN'S NOTE:

● This bread is very high in fibre and is hence a very dense, heavy bread. It is more like the German breads than our standard sponge-like breads. Good for **carbo-loading**.
● No process should ever take more than 2–3 minutes, and the total whipping and mixing time per recipe should never exceed 5 minutes, as this raises the GI.

Bran and oat loaf, and Fruit and nut muesli

TRAIL MUESLI
Makes 500 g (10 x 50 g servings)

180 g (2 cups) rolled oats
90 g (1 cup) whole-wheat Pronutro
60 ml (¼ cup) Hi-Fibre Bran cereal
45 ml (3 T) sultanas
60 ml (¼ cup) dried pears, peaches,
  apricots or apple, chopped
80 ml (⅓ cup) mixed nuts,
  chopped roughly
60 ml (¼ cup) skim milk powder
125 ml (½ cup) brown sugar

NUTRIENTS PER SERVING

Glycaemic index 56 ● Fat 5 g
Carbohydrate 28 g ● Fibre 6 g
Protein 6 g ● kJ 789

ONE 50 g SERVING is equivalent to
just under 2 STARCH and 1 FAT

1 Mix all the ingredients together.
2 Store in an airtight container.
3 Serve with low-fat milk, or water.

DIETICIAN'S NOTE:
● This muesli was especially formulated to be eaten with water to make it more convenient for **hikers, campers** and **travellers**.
● It is suitable for **diabetics** as well, served either with water or with low-fat milk.
● With water the GI is 56.
● With low-fat milk the GI is lowered.
● This muesli is also suitable for **carbo-loading** as it contains a good proportion of low-GI carbohydrate and not too much protein and fat. For carbo-loading purposes it is best eaten with water.

GRIDDLE CAKES
Makes 10 griddle cakes

125 ml (½ cup) flour, sifted
  before measuring
15 ml (3 t) baking powder
2.5 ml (½ t) salt
2 eggs
250 ml (1 cup) leftover cooked oat
  porridge
100 ml (⅖ cup) oat bran
5 ml (1 t) canola or olive oil
250 ml (1 cup) low-fat milk

NUTRIENTS PER CAKE

Glycaemic index 59 ● Fat 3 g
Carbohydrate 10 g ● Fibre 1 g
Protein 4 g ● kJ 355

One GRIDDLE CAKE is equivalent to
1 STARCH and ½ FAT

1 Sift flour, baking powder and salt together.
2 Beat the eggs.
3 Add eggs, oat porridge, oat bran and oil to the flour mixture, and beat until fluffy, but for no longer than 1–2 minutes, as the GI is raised by beating. Add enough milk to give a dropping consistency to the batter.
4 Bake tablespoonfuls in a hot non-stick pan, or in a frying pan that has been lightly sprayed with cooking spray.
5 Serve with low-fat grated cheese, a poached egg, Bovril or Marmite, apricot jam or marmalade. DO NOT SPREAD with margarine or butter. Simply add the topping.

DIETICIAN'S NOTE:
● The toppings are not included in the nutritional analysis.
● Two low-GI ingredients (oat porridge and oat bran) have been added to the batter of these griddle cakes and the GI is still not below 55. This is because of the flour.
● **As soon as flour is part of a recipe, the GI goes up.**
● If the flour is sifted before measuring, the danger of using too much is lessened.

SPECIAL CRUMPETS
Makes about 20 crumpets (6 cm diameter)

1 egg, lightly beaten
10 ml (2 t) sugar
2 ml (½ t) salt
250 ml (1 cup) low-fat or fat-free milk
5 ml (1 t) canola or sunflower oil
250 ml (1 cup; 120 g) cake flour, sifted
   before measuring
5 ml (1 t) bicarbonate of soda
5 ml (1 t) baking powder
125 ml (½ cup) oat bran
1 large apple, grated with the skin

NUTRIENTS PER CRUMPET

Glycaemic index 60 ● Fat 1 g
Carbohydrate 8 g ● Fibre 0.6 g
Protein 2 g ● kJ 213

ONE CRUMPET is equivalent to
½ STARCH

1 Beat the egg with a hand whisk in a mixing bowl.
2 Add the sugar and salt and beat for not more than 1 minute.
3 Add half the milk and the oil. Beat for not more than 1 minute.
4 Sift together the flour, bicarbonate and baking powder and stir gradually into the egg and milk mixture with a wooden spoon until smooth and lump free. Do not overmix.
5 Add the rest of the milk, the oat bran and the grated apple and mix gently. Leave the batter to stand for 10 minutes to moisten all the ingredients.
6 Heat a non-stick frying pan and spray with cooking spray. Ladle about 4 separate tablespoons of batter into pan and cook the four crumpets over moderate to high heat until bubbly on top and light brown underneath. Turn to brown on other side. Repeat with the remaining batter.

DIETICIAN'S NOTE:

● There is no need to spread these crumpets with margarine or butter. Eat dry with a little marmalade or apricot jam and low-fat cheese, if desired.
● Be careful not to beat this batter too much. Beating improves digestibility and thus would increase the GI of the crumpets.
● It is **very important to add the apple**, as this is the vital ingredient that lowers the GI of the crumpets.

 # HEALTHY OAT BREAD
Cuts into 14 slices

150 ml (⅗ cup) oats
250 ml (1 cup) oat bran
375 ml (1½ cups) flour, sifted
   before measuring
250 ml (1 cup) whole-wheat Pronutro
5 ml (1 t) salt
20 ml (4 t) baking powder
20 ml (4 t) sugar
1 egg
200 ml (⅘ cup) low-fat milk
25 ml (2 D) water

NUTRIENTS PER SLICE

Glycaemic index 61 ● Fat 2 g
Carbohydrate 20 g ● Fibre 3 g
Protein 5 g ● kJ 515

ONE SLICE OF BREAD is equivalent to
1½ STARCH

1 In a large bowl, mix the oats, oat bran, flour, Pronutro, baking powder, salt and sugar.
2 Beat egg, milk and water together for not longer than 1 minute.
3 Combine the egg mixture with the flour mixture and stir until dry ingredients are just moistened.
4 Work the dough into a soft ball with your hands, using more oats to prevent it from sticking to your hands. Cover the ball of dough with oats and form into a round loaf shape. Place on a baking sheet and bake for about 1 hour at 180 °C.

To check if the loaf is done, tap the bread with your knuckle. If it sounds hollow, it is baked through and ready to take out the oven. A very easy bread to enjoy at a braai or with soup.
This bread freezes well, whole or sliced. Each slice can be thawed in a toaster as and when required.

DIETICIAN'S NOTE:

● The flour, having high GI, has to be substituted with the lower GI oats, oat bran and whole-wheat Pronutro. This results in a heavier, yet very tasty bread. However, it must be eaten fresh.
● An excellent bread for **lowering cholesterol** because it has a high oat and oat bran content.

Special crumpets, and Healthy oat bread

BREAKFAST OAT BAPS

Makes 15 flat soft rolls

500 ml (2 cups) oats
375 ml (1½ cups) low-fat milk, warmed
10 ml (2 t) instant dry yeast
30 ml (2 T) sugar
50 ml (4 D) 'lite' margarine, melted
5 ml (1 t) salt
375 ml (1½ cups) cake flour, sifted
    before measuring
125 ml (½ cup) whole-wheat Pronutro

NUTRIENTS PER SLICE

Glycaemic index 62 ● Fat 4 g
Carbohydrate 20 g ● Fibre 2 g
Protein 4 g ● kJ 552

ONE BAP is equivalent to 1½ STARCH
and ½ FAT

1 Place the oats in a glass bowl, add warm milk and leave to soak for 30 minutes.
2 Dissolve yeast and 10 ml of the sugar in 50 ml warm water and leave until frothy.
3 To the oats mixture, add the yeast mixture, sugar, margarine, salt, flour and Pronutro. Stir to form a very stiff dough. Add warm water, if necessary, but not more than 50 ml.
4 On a floured surface knead the dough into a soft ball, using more oats to prevent the dough from sticking to your hands. Place the dough in a mixing bowl, cover with cling wrap, and leave to rise for 1 hour, or prove in the microwave oven (see below) until doubled in volume.
5 Knock back by kneading, then shape into 15 rolls. Place on an ungreased baking tray, cover with a damp, clean cloth and leave in a warm place, or an oven at 50–60 °C, until doubled in size.
6 Dust with flour and bake at 220 °C for about 25 minutes.
7 Eat fresh, or freeze and heat in the oven at 120 °C to thaw.

When working with yeast, it is very important that all the ingredients should be warm.
To prove yeast dough in the microwave: Place the dough in a glass or ceramic mixing bowl and cover with cling wrap. Microwave on high for 20 seconds, and repeat every 15 minutes until the dough has doubled in size (about 1 hour). Leave the dough in the microwave during this time.

DIETICIAN'S NOTE:
● To lower the GI, we had to substitute at least half of the flour with low-GI oats and whole-wheat Pronutro. This results in more dense rolls that are not as well risen, in fact, they are more like baps. But they are very tasty and well worth the effort as their GI is substantially lower than bought rolls. For hamburger buns, make them twice as big.

TROPICAL FRUIT MUESLI

Makes 500 g (10 x 50 g servings)

225 g (2½ cups) rolled oats
75 g (1½ cups) Hi-Fibre Bran cereal
50 g (1 cup) All-Bran Flakes
25 g (2 T) raisins
75 g dried fruit flakes
50 g (5 T) sultanas
60 ml (¼ cup) chopped dried apple

NUTRIENTS PER SERVING

Glycaemic index 59 ● Fat 3 g
Carbohydrate 28 g ● Fibre 9 g
Protein 5 g ● kJ 702

ONE 50 g SERVING is equivalent to
2 STARCH and ½ FAT

1 Mix all the ingredients.
2 Store in an airtight container.
3 Serve with low-fat milk

We found it much easier to make double or treble the recipe at one time as the muesli keeps very well.

DIETICIAN'S NOTE:
● When eaten with milk the GI of this muesli breakfast dish is lowered to less than 55.
● This muesli is suitable for **carbo-loading** as it has a good low-GI carbohydrate content with little fat and protein.
● This is the best option for **slimmers** as it only contains the tiny bit of fat found in wholegrain cereals. Serve with skim milk.

Tropical fruit muesli, and Breakfast oat baps

DATE AND OAT MUFFINS
Makes 12 muffins

250 ml (1 cup) whole-wheat flour
250 ml (1 cup) oat bran
10 ml (2 t) baking powder
2 ml (½ t) ground cinnamon
1 ml (¼ t) ground nutmeg
1 ml (¼ t) ground cloves
45 ml (3 T) 'lite' margarine
1 large apple, peeled and grated
125 ml (½ cup) chopped dates
150 ml (⅗ cup) skim milk
15 ml (1 T) brown sugar
2 egg whites, whisked to soft-peak stage

1 Preheat the oven to 200 °C.
2 Sift the flour and add back the bran. Add the oat bran, baking powder, cinnamon, nutmeg and cloves. Gently mix with a spoon, lifting up the flour mix to incorporate air.
3 Rub in the margarine.
4 Add the apple and dates. Mix well, but for not more than 1 minute.
5 Add the milk and brown sugar, then fold in the stiffly beaten egg whites.
6 Spoon into sprayed muffin pans and bake in the preheated oven for 15–20 minutes.

DIETICIAN'S NOTE:

● Compare this recipe with the Bran Muffins (page 38) where we use a whole cup of sugar. The latter actually has a lower glycaemic index! We hope this convinces you that sugar is not always the baddie we thought it was in the past.

NUTRIENTS PER MUFFIN

Glycaemic index 60 ● Fat 3 g
Carbohydrate 20 g ● Fibre 3 g
Protein 4 g ● kJ 533

ONE MUFFIN is equivalent to 1 STARCH, 1 FRUIT, and ½ FAT

WHOLE-WHEAT OAT MUFFINS
Makes 12 muffins

250 ml (1 cup) oats
250 ml (1 cup) oat bran
250 ml (1 cup) whole-wheat flour
250 ml (1 cup) bran
60 ml (4 T) sugar
2 ml (½ t) salt
20 ml (4 t) baking powder
1 large grated apple DO NOT LEAVE OUT
30 ml (2 T) 'lite' margarine
250 ml (1 cup) skim milk
2 eggs, use only one of the yolks, but both egg whites
120 ml apricot jam for spreading on the muffins. See DIETICIAN'S NOTE

1 Mix all the dry ingredients with the grated apple. With the spoon, lift the mixture a few times to incorporate air.
2 Rub the margarine into the dry ingredients until the mixture resembles fine bread crumbs.
3 Beat eggs and milk together and add to the other ingredients to form a soft mixture. Do not overmix.
4 Spoon into a greased muffin pan.
5 Bake at 180 °C for 15 minutes.
6 Serve WITHOUT margarine or butter. Simply cut each muffin in half and top with 2 level teaspoons apricot jam per muffin.

DIETICIAN'S NOTE:

● The analysis on the left is for the muffin without any jam. If we **add the jam** as instructed, the GI is lowered to 55! In this case the apricot jam actually lowers the GI because apricots are so slowly absorbed and have a lower GI than flour. If eaten with jam, the **Jack Spratt** will change to **Green**!
● SO ... sometimes adding jam to a muffin can be beneficial, as it slows down the absorption of the carbohydrates.
● With the jam, these muffins are good for **carbo-loading**.
● Adding 2 heaped teaspoons grated, low-fat Cheddar cheese per muffin would increase the fat to 6 g of fat per portion, which is still within reasonable limits.

NUTRIENTS PER MUFFIN

Glycaemic index 57 ● Fat 4 g
Carbohydrate 23 g ● Fibre 5 g
Protein 6 g ● kJ 649

● ONE MUFFIN (NO cheese or jam) is equivalent to 2 STARCH and ½ FAT
● ONE MUFFIN with JAM is equivalent to 2½ STARCH, ½ FAT
● ONE MUFFIN with CHEESE is equivalent to 2 STARCH, ½ FAT and ⅓ PROTEIN

BRAN MUFFINS

Makes 24 large muffins. NOTE: This batter has to stand overnight.

2 eggs
150 g (1 cup) soft brown sugar
60 ml (4 T) canola oil
250 ml (1 cup) oat bran, pressed down
    into the cup
375 ml (1½ cups) flour, sifted before
    measuring
500 ml (2 cups) digestive bran
2 ml (½ t) salt
15 ml (1 T) bicarbonate of soda
1 large grated apple
250 ml (1 cup) sultanas
5 ml (1 t) ground cinnamon
500 ml (2 cups) low-fat milk
5 ml (1 t) vanilla essence

1 Beat together eggs, sugar and oil.
2 Add all the dry ingredients, the grated apple and the sultanas. Mix thoroughly, lifting the mixture a few times with the spoon to incorporate air.
3 Mix the milk and vanilla and add to the flour mixture. Stir until well blended, but do not overmix. Leave overnight in the refrigerator.
4 When ready to bake, stir and drop into muffin pan and bake at 180 °C for 15 minutes.

This mixture can be kept in the refrigerator for up to 30 days. Do not freeze the batter.
Baked muffins freeze very well.

DIETICIAN'S NOTE:
● These muffins are deliciously moist and do not need to be spread with margarine or butter.
● Despite all the oat bran and the bran – we have loaded these muffins as much as we could without sacrificing texture – the GI is still 58. It is the FLOUR that does this, NOT the sugar. Even if we halve the sugar, the GI only comes down by 1 point!

NUTRIENTS PER MUFFIN

Glycaemic index 58 ● Fat 3 g
Carbohydrate 22 g ● Fibre 3 g
Protein 3 g ● kJ 507

ONE MUFFIN is equivalent to 1 STARCH,
1 FRUIT and ½ FAT

CHEESE AND HERB SCONES

Makes 12 scones. No need to butter, or to add any other topping to these scones – they are delicious as they are!

150 g (1 cup) self-raising flour, sifted
    before measuring
7.5 ml (1½ t) baking powder
120 g (1 cup, pressed down) oat bran
1 grated apple, unpeeled
    DO NOT LEAVE OUT
45 ml (3 T) 'lite' margarine
125 ml (½ cup) low-fat milk
30 ml (2 T) water
60 g (2 matchboxes) low-fat Cheddar or
    mozzarella cheese, grated
25 ml (2 T) fresh parsley, chopped
25 ml (2 T) fresh basil, chopped, or
    5 ml (1 t) dried basil
5 ml (1 t) dried rosemary
10 ml (2 t) grated Parmesan
25 ml (2 T) chutney, 'lite' or ordinary

1 Sift the flour and baking powder into a large bowl, stir in the oat bran and grated apple, lifting the mixture a few times with the spoon to incorporate air. Rub in the margarine.
2 Make a well in the centre. Add milk and water. Mix lightly with a knife, adding extra water if necessary, to make a soft dough.
3 Turn the dough onto a lightly floured board and knead gently, using the fingertips only. Roll out to a rectangle about 1 cm thick. Scatter half the cheese and all the herbs over the entire surface.
4 Beginning from a long side roll up like a swiss roll to make a thick sausage. Cut into 2 cm slices to make little rounds. Place the rounds side by side on a greased baking tray, spread with a little chutney and then sprinkle with the remaining cheeses.
5 Bake in a preheated oven at 200 °C for 20 minutes or until golden brown. Do not to bake too long as they dry out easily.
6 Serve hot or cold.

DIETICIAN'S NOTE:
● These savoury scones also make a delicious light lunch if served with a tossed salad.
● They are also ideal as a tasty snack.
● Despite the substitution of half the flour with the oat bran, the GI is still higher than we aimed at. In real life, however, these muffins showed a much slower absorption rate, therefore we feel they are quite safe.

NUTRIENTS PER SCONE

Glycaemic index 61 ● Fat 5 g
Carbohydrate 16 g ● Fibre 2 g
Protein 5 g ● kJ 551

One SERVING is equivalent to
1 STARCH, ½ PROTEIN and ½ FAT

MOCK PUMPKIN SOUP

Serves 8 starter portions or 4 meal portions

5 ml (1 t) canola or olive oil
1 large onion, coarsely chopped
3 medium sweet potatoes, peeled and
    chopped
250 ml (1 cup) dry white wine
1 chicken stock cube or 20ml stock
    powder dissolved in
500 ml (2 cups) boiling water
bunch fresh basil or 2.5 ml (½ t) dried basil
250 ml (1 cup) low-fat milk
1 ml (¼ t) ground cinnamon
freshly ground black pepper

1 Heat oil in a saucepan, add the onion and cook over medium heat for 5 minutes.
2 Add the sweet potato, wine and stock; simmer, covered, for 20–30 minutes until the sweet potato is soft.
3 Add the basil leaves and puree the soup in a food processor or blender for not longer than one minute.
4 Return to the saucepan, add the milk, cinnamon and pepper to taste and reheat.
5 Serve as a starter or light meal.

This soup is a good replacement for the usual high-GI pumpkin soup. If serving for starters, use one ladle per portion. For a meal use 2 ladles per portion.

NUTRIENTS PER MEAL SERVING

Glycaemic index 48 ● Fat 3 g
Carbohydrate 56 g ● Fibre 8 g
Protein 7 g ● kJ 1448

ONE SERVING is equivalent to 3 STARCH,
1 LIMITED VEGETABLE and ½ PROTEIN/DAIRY

DIETICIAN'S NOTE:

● The nutrient analysis given alongside is for a meal portion. For starters, all the values are halved.
● Using sweet potato in this recipe not only effectively lowers the GI of the soup, but it also gives the soup a delicious flavour.
● This soup is ideal for **carbo-loading** as it contains lots of sustained release carbohydrate and very little protein and fat.

TOMATO AND BARLEY SOUP

Serves 6

5 ml (1 t) canola or olive oil
1 large onion, finely chopped
2 cloves garlic, crushed or
    10 ml (2 t) minced garlic
5 ml (1 t) curry powder
1 chicken stock cube dissolved in
1.5 litres (6 cups) boiling water
250 ml (1 cup) split lentils or
    red lentils
125 ml (½ cup) pearl barley
1 x 410 g tin tomatoes, chopped with
    the juice
freshly ground black pepper
chopped fresh parsley, to serve

1 Heat the oil in a large saucepan. Add the onion and garlic and stir while cooking gently until just brown.
2 Add curry powder and cook, stirring for 1 minute.
3 Stir in the water, stock, lentils, barley, tomatoes, and pepper to taste. Bring to boil and simmer for 45 minutes to one hour until the lentils and barley are tender.
4 Sprinkle with freshly chopped parsley and serve with Bran and oat loaf (page 28) or Healthy oat bread (page 32), if desired.

A delicious tomato soup with a hint of curry.
A tasty and filling winter soup that is a meal in itself.

NUTRIENTS PER SERVING

Glycaemic index 22 ● Fat 2 g
Carbohydrate 28 g ● Fibre 8 g
Protein 12 g ● kJ 833

ONE SERVING is equivalent to
1½ STARCH, 1 PROTEIN and
FREE VEGETABLE.

DIETICIAN'S NOTE:

● Barley has a low GI and is rich in soluble fibre and is very effective in **binding cholesterol** as well as lowering morning blood glucose readings in **diabetics**.
● This soup has such a low GI that it can be enjoyed with a slice of ordinary bought bread, if desired. Remember to count the extra STARCH if you have the bread.
● For **carbo-loading** use a double portion with 2 slices of bread. This meal would then contribute 86 g carbohydrates.

Mock pumpkin soup, and Tomato and barley soup

MINESTRONE SOUP
Serves 6

5 ml (1 t) canola or olive oil
2 onions, chopped
2 cloves garlic, crushed or
    10 ml (2 t) minced garlic
2 rashers of lean bacon, all visible fat
    removed, chopped
1 x 410 g tin small white beans, drained
1 beef stock cube or
    20 ml (4 t) stock powder dissolved in
1.5 litres (6 cups) water
2 carrots, diced
2 sticks celery, sliced
2 baby marrows, chopped
3 tomatoes, diced

100 g (1 cup) small durum wheat pasta shapes
30 ml (2 T) chopped parsley
freshly ground black pepper to taste

1 Heat the oil in a large saucepan and add the onion, garlic and bacon. Cook for 5 minutes or until soft.
2 Add the beans, stock cube and water and simmer for 15 minutes.
3 Add the vegetables and simmer for another 30 minutes.
4 Add the pasta and simmer, uncovered, for 10–15 minutes until the pasta is tender. Stir in the parsley and pepper to taste.
5 Serve with a sprinkling of Parmesan cheese if desired.

DIETICIAN'S NOTE:

● This soup is so low in GI that it can be eaten with ordinary bought bread. For slimmers, remember to add another STARCH if you have the bread.
● By leaving out the pasta, the soup will contain 1 PROTEIN and FREE VEGETABLES Add a slice of bread and you have the perfect **slimmers meal**.
● For **carbo-loading**, have a double portion of soup, with two slices of bread. The meal would then contain 80 g carbohydrates.

NUTRIENTS PER SERVING
Glycaemic index 28 ● Fat 3 g
Carbohydrate 26 g ● Fibre 7 g
Protein 8 g ● kJ 694

ONE SERVING is equivalent to 1 STARCH, 1 PROTEIN and FREE VEGETABLES

GOURMET VEGETABLE SOUP
Serves 10

5 ml (1 t) canola or olive oil
2 carrots, cut into strips
500 ml (2 cups) cabbage, coarsely
    chopped
2 onions, chopped
2 leeks, sliced
1 stalk of celery, chopped
2 tomatoes, peeled and chopped
1 x 410 g tin brown or sugar beans,
    drained
1 litre (4 cups) water
2 ml (½ t) salt
10 ml (2 t) Worcestershire sauce
freshly ground black pepper to taste
10 slices French bread
60 g low-fat mozzarella cheese, grated
    (2 matchboxes cheese)

1 For the soup: Heat oil in a large saucepan and add vegetables. Sauté over low heat for 10 minutes, stirring occasionally.
2 Add the beans, 500 ml water and flavouring. Simmer for about 30 minutes, or until the vegetables are soft.
3 For the topping: Lightly toast the slices of bread in a toaster.
4 Remove 60 ml (½ cup) of the vegetables from the soup and mash or process in a food processor for not more than 1 minute.
5 Spread the mashed vegetables on the slices of toasted bread, and sprinkle with grated cheese. Arrange on a baking tray and bake under the grill until golden brown.
6 Mash the remaining vegetables or process in a food processor for not more than 1 minute. Add the remaining water and simmer to a smooth consistency. Serve hot, with the slices of bread floating on top, or served separately.

DIETICIAN'S NOTE:

● This is a delicious hearty meal on its own.
● This soup is ideal for **carbo-loading** as it has a low GI, high carbohydrate content with not too much protein, and is very low in fat as well. A double portion would yield 32 g carbohydrates. If bread is needed with the meal, use a low-GI bread and NOT normal bought bread because the GI of the soup is already higher due to the French bread topping.

NUTRIENTS PER SERVING
Glycaemic index 46 ● Fat 2 g
Carbohydrate 16 g ● Fibre 5 g
Protein 6 g ● kJ 492

ONE SERVING is equivalent to 1 STARCH, ½ PROTEIN, and FREE VEGETABLES

Gourmet vegetable soup, and Minestrone soup

LENTIL SOUP
Serves 10

1 x 410 g tin chickpeas
1 vegetable stock cube or
   20 ml (4 t) stock powder, dissolved in
2 litres (8 cups) boiling water
1 large onion, chopped
10 ml (2 t) sugar
1 x 410 g tin chopped tomatoes
2 (100 g) celery stalks and leaves, sliced
1 x 65 g tin tomato paste
freshly ground black pepper
3 ml (½ t) ground ginger
5 ml (1 t) ground cinnamon
200 g (1 cup) large green or brown lentils
   soaked in hot water for 1 hour, or
2 x 410 g tin brown or green lentils

20ml (4 t) lemon juice (juice of ½ lemon)
6 baby marrows, sliced (500 g)
100 g (1½ cups) durum wheat spaghetti,
   broken into 4 cm pieces
chopped parsley for garnishing

1 Drain the chickpeas and place in a large saucepan with the stock, water, onion, sugar, tomatoes, celery and tomato paste. Simmer for 20 minutes and then add salt and pepper to taste.
2 Add ginger, cinnamon and lentils and cook for 20 minutes until lentils are soft.
3 Add the lemon juice, baby marrows and pasta and add more water, if necessary. Cook for 15 minutes. Just before serving, stir in the parsley.

NUTRIENTS PER SERVING

Glycaemic index 27 ● Fat 1 g
Carbohydrate 24 g ● Fibre 8 g
Protein 9 g ● kJ 679

ONE SERVING is equivalent to 1 STARCH,
1 PROTEIN and FREE VEGETABLES

DIETICIAN'S NOTE:

● This is an ideal **carbo-loading** meal if combined with two slices of bread. Soup and two slices of bread would contribute 54 g of carbohydrate.
● The GI of this soup is low enough to allow ordinary bought bread with the soup. Remember to count the extra STARCH.

CREAMY CHICKEN AND MUSHROOM SOUP
Serves 4 (large servings)

250 ml (1 cup) oats
5 ml (1 t) canola or olive oil
2 large onions, diced
1 clove garlic, crushed
50 ml (⅕ cup) dry white wine
1 chicken stock cube or
   20 ml (4 t) stock powder
1 x 410 g tin low-fat evaporated milk
1½ tins water (630 ml)
2 chicken breasts, cooked and diced
   (220 g cooked chicken)
250 g mushrooms, sliced (1 punnet)
pinch of marjoram or origanum
few drops of soya sauce

1 In a dry saucepan, stir the oats over low heat until browned. Remove from the saucepan and set aside.
2 Heat the oil in the saucepan and sauté the onion and garlic, stirring constantly, until the onion becomes transparent.
3 Stir in the browned oats, wine, milk and stock cube.
4 Add 1½ tins of water using the evaporated milk tin, swirling out the milk left over in the tin.
5 Add the chopped chicken and mushrooms and simmer for 5–10 minutes, stirring to prevent the soup from scorching on the bottom of the saucepan.
6 Season to taste with marjoram and soya sauce.
7 Serve with freshly made Breakfast oat baps (page 34), Bran and oat loaf (page 28) or Healthy oat bread (page 32), if desired.

This recipe makes 4 large servings, a serving being a meal in itself. Bread, or rolls, is only required for the very hungry. As a starter it will serve 6.

NUTRIENTS PER SERVING

Glycaemic index 36 ● Fat 10 g
Carbohydrate 32 g ● Fibre 4 g
Protein 28 g ● kJ 1477

ONE SERVING is equivalent to 1 STARCH,
2 PROTEIN and 1 DAIRY

DIETICIAN'S NOTE:

● For such a really creamy soup, the low fat and high fibre content is exceptional.

FLAGEOLET VINAIGRETTE (WHITE-BEAN SALAD)

Serves 4

1 x 410 g tin small white beans
3–4 leeks, thinly sliced
½ green or red pepper, seeded and
    chopped
1 large stick table celery, sliced
100 ml (⅖ cup) chopped parsley
10 ml (2 t) sugar
2 tomatoes
60 g feta cheese (2 matchboxes)
6–8 black olives

DRESSING
12.5 ml (1 D) canola or olive oil
1 clove garlic
25 ml (2 D) lemon juice
5 ml (1 t) dried origanum
½ vegetable stock cube or 10 ml (1 t)
    stock powder
125 ml (½ cup) boiling water

1 Make the dressing by mixing all the ingredients.
2 In a glass bowl, microwave the beans for 2 minutes on high.
3 Add the salad dressing to the beans and mix lightly with a fork, taking care not to break up the beans.
4 Add the leeks, pepper, celery, parsley and sugar to the bean mixture. Mix gently.
5 Cover and chill for at least 2 hours or chill overnight.
6 To serve, adjust seasoning of bean salad with salt and pepper if needed.
7 Spoon onto a large flat platter. Surround the heap of bean salad with thickly sliced tomatoes and crumble the feta cheese on top of the beans.
8 Place a few olives on the salad to finish it off. Serve as a meal.

DIETICIAN'S NOTE:
● An unusual, appetizing, well-balanced meal on its own. Easy to prepare for those unexpected guests on the weekend.

NUTRIENTS PER SERVING

Glycaemic index 30 ● Fat 7 g
Carbohydrate 17 g ● Fibre 8 g
Protein 8 g ● kJ 775

ONE SERVING is equivalent to 1 STARCH, 1 PROTEIN and 1 LIMITED VEGETABLE

BROCCOLI AND MUSHROOM SALAD WITH COTTAGE CHEESE DRESSING

Serves 6–8

500 g broccoli or cauliflower
salt and freshly ground black pepper
250 g mushrooms, wiped and sliced
    (one punnet)
4 spring onions, chopped
250 g smooth, fat-free cottage cheese
175 ml plain or flavoured low-fat yoghurt
50 ml (4 D) 'lite' mayonnaise
60 ml (¼ cup) chopped parsley
10 ml (2 t) honey
1 ml (¼ t) celery salt
1–2 pickled gherkins, chopped
paprika

1 Trim broccoli or cauliflower and slice lengthwise. Poach in a little boiling water until just tender.
2 Drain, chop coarsely and arrange in a large shallow salad bowl or platter. Season and then add the sliced mushrooms.
3 In a separate bowl, mix the spring onions, cottage cheese, yoghurt, mayonnaise, parsley, honey, celery salt and gherkins.
4 Stir until well blended, adding a little skim milk if the dressing is too thick.
5 Pour over the broccoli (or cauliflower) and mushrooms and dust with paprika.
6 Chill until required.
7 Serve at room temperature.

This appetizing salad is very low in fat and adds variety to a buffet. Apricot-flavoured yoghurt will add an interesting tang to the dressing.

DIETICIAN'S NOTE:
● Broccoli is one of the most vitamin-dense vegetables around. It is full of anti-oxidants, and fibre as well. We should all try to eat broccoli every day.

NUTRIENTS PER SERVING

Glycaemic index 25 ● Fat 2 g
Carbohydrate 10 g ● Fibre 3 g
Protein 10 g ● kJ 434

ONE SERVING is equivalent to 1 DAIRY and FREE VEGETABLES

Broccoli and mushroom salad with cottage cheese dressing, and Flageolet vinaigrette (white-bean salad)

QUICK BEAN AND NOODLE SALAD
Serves 6

1 x 410 g tin baked beans in
    tomato sauce
250 g (2 cups) cooked small-shell
    durum wheat noodles
50 ml (4 D) 'lite' salad cream or
    'lite' mayonnaise (low-oil dressing)
50 ml (4 D) 'lite' fruit chutney or
    ordinary chutney
½ onion, chopped
½ green pepper, diced
3 'lite' viennas, sliced
black pepper, freshly ground
lettuce leaves

NUTRIENTS PER SERVING

Glycaemic index 38 ● Fat 4 g
Carbohydrate 27 g ● Fibre 7 g
Protein 9 g ● kJ 739

ONE SERVING is equivalent to
1½ STARCH and 1 PROTEIN

1 Mix the beans with the cooked shell noodles.
2 Fold in the mayonnaise and chutney.
3 Add the onion, green peppers and viennas.
4 Season to taste, mix well and chill.
5 Serve on lettuce leaves.

This is a very quick and easy salad to make, and a meal in itself.
This salad can be served hot or cold

DIETICIAN'S NOTE:

● By doubling up the noodles, this salad makes a delicious **carbo-loading** meal which contains 38 g carbohydrate and has a GI of 33.
● It is important to use the lower-fat viennas to keep the fat low.
● Legumes and pasta make a wonderful, low-GI combination. Remember this when choosing salads at a salad bar in a restaurant. Avoid the high-fat salad dressings by 'draining' the salad as much as possible.

GREEN-BEAN SALAD
Serves 12

1 x 410 g tin of butter beans
1 x 410 g tin of green beans
1 x 410 g tin of garden peas
1 onion, finely chopped
2 tomatoes, chopped
½ green pepper, finely chopped (optional)
15 ml (1 T) canola or olive oil
30 ml (2 T) lemon juice
10 ml (2 t) sugar
5 ml (1 t) mixed herbs
freshly ground black pepper to taste

NUTRIENTS PER SERVING

Glycaemic index 35 ● Fat 1 g
Carbohydrate 8 g ● Fibre 3 g
Protein 3 g ● kJ 277

ONE SERVING is equivalent to 1 LIMITED
VEGETABLE and 1 FREE VEGETABLE

1 Drain the beans and peas and mix with the onion, tomatoes and green pepper. Reserve.
2 Mix the remaining ingredients.
3 Shake well and pour over the bean and pea mixture.
4 Chill overnight to enhance the flavour.

This salad will keep for up to two weeks in the refrigerator.
It is ideal to make in advance for a braai, picnic, camping and even for self-catering holidays.

DIETICIAN'S NOTE:

● A wonderfully easy, low-fat salad that can be made in advance and served at very short notice.
● Of all the legumes, butter beans are probably the most versatile. They are creamier in texture than other dried beans and have a pleasant nutty flavour. This makes them ideal for adding to all salads, stir-fries, stews, curries and casseroles.

CHILLED TUNA SALAD

Serves 5

250 ml (1 cup) uncooked pearl wheat, or
   750 ml (3 cups) cooked pearl wheat
   (stampkoring)
½ green pepper, finely chopped
½ onion, finely chopped
2 x 170 g tins of tuna chunks in brine,
   drained and flaked
10 black olives
3 large tomatoes, diced
125 ml (½ cup) 'lite' mayonnaise
25 ml (2 D) 'lite' tomato sauce, or
   ordinary tomato sauce
2 ml (½ t) marjoram
25 ml (2 D) chopped parsley
freshly ground black pepper

NUTRIENTS PER SERVING

Glycaemic index 33 ● Fat 5 g
Carbohydrate 19 g ● Fibre 4 g
Protein 18 g ● kJ 844

ONE SERVING is equivalent to 1 STARCH
and 2 PROTEIN

1 Cook the pearl wheat in lots of water until tender. Drain.
2 Add the green pepper, onions, tuna, olives and tomatoes. Mix gently until combined.
3 Mix mayonnaise and tomato sauce with the marjoram and pour over the salad. Mix the parsley in last.
4 Season to taste with pepper. Chill.
5 Serve on a bed of lettuce with Bran and oat loaf (page 28), Healthy oat bread (page 32) or Breakfast oat baps (page 34).

DIETICIAN'S NOTE:

● Since the tomato sauce is such a minor ingredient, and its GI is low, any type of tomato sauce may be used.
● In summer this salad makes a wonderful lunch. It can easily be made in the morning and then chilled until the children return home from school.
● For **slimmers** this is the ideal lunch. The very low GI ensures good blood-glucose levels and prevents that mid-afternoon craving for a snack.

PIQUANT THREE BEAN SALAD

Serves 12

1 x 410 g tin butter beans, drained
1 x 410 g tin baked beans in
   tomato sauce
1 x 410 g tin French-cut green beans,
   drained
15 ml (1 T) sugar
2 ml (½ t) mustard powder
15 ml (1 T) canola or olive oil
100 ml (⅖ cup) white or
   brown vinegar
5 ml (1 t) dried basil
freshly ground black pepper to taste

NUTRIENTS PER SERVING

Glycaemic index 44 ● Fat 1 g
Carbohydrate 11 g ● Fibre 5 g
Protein 4 g ● kJ 322

ONE SERVING is equivalent to ½ STARCH
and 1 LIMITED VEGETABLE

1 Mix the three tins of beans.
2 Heat sugar, mustard powder, oil, vinegar and basil in a saucepan until the sugar has dissolved. Stir continuously.
3 Pour the sauce over the bean mixture.
4 Season with pepper to taste and mix well.
5 Chill overnight or for at least 3 hours.
6 Serve cold.

This salad will keep for as long as two weeks in a sealed container in the refrigerator.
It is ideal for making in advance for picnics, camping and even for self-catering holidays.

DIETICIAN'S NOTE:

● Half a portion is equal to 1 LIMITED VEGETABLE
● This very low-fat salad goes well with all outdoor meals.
● For **diabetics** this low-GI salad is ideal to take along to a 'bring-and-braai'.
● Even if the sugar is doubled, it hardly affects the GI.

Piquant three bean salad, and Chilled tuna salad

CABBAGE AND APPLE SALAD
Serves 4

1 red apple
1 green apple
10–20 ml (2–4 t) lemon juice
500 ml (2 cups) cabbage, finely
    chopped or grated
60 ml (4 T) plain, low-fat yoghurt
125 ml (½ cup) low-oil salad cream or
    low-oil mayonnaise
10 ml (2 t) sunflower seeds
4 lettuce leaves

1 Wash the apples, but do not peel them. Slice thinly or cube. Sprinkle with just enough lemon juice to prevent discolouration.
2 Add the apple to the cabbage and lightly mix with a fork.
3 For the dressing, mix the yoghurt, low-oil salad cream and sunflower seeds. Add 5–15 ml sugar if too tart.
4 Pour the dressing over the cabbage and apple, toss the salad and spoon into a container with a lid. Chill for 2 hours or longer before use.
5 Serve the salad on the lettuce leaves.

DIETICIAN'S NOTE:
● This is a deliciously different coleslaw, lower in fat than the traditional one.
● This salad can be made the day before, covered and kept in the refrigerator until it is ready for serving.
● This recipe makes 4 large portions or 6 smaller portions. The analysis is for the 4 large portions.

NUTRIENTS PER SERVING
Glycaemic index <25 ● Fat 4 g
Carbohydrate 11 g ● Fibre 2 g
Protein 2 g ● kJ 375

ONE SERVING is equivalent to 1 FAT, 1 FRUIT and FREE VEGETABLES

BABY POTATO SALAD
Serves 8

1 kg baby or new potatoes
250 ml (1 cup) young green beans,
    sliced
500 ml (2 cups) cherry tomatoes
½ English cucumber, chopped
90 g low-fat feta cheese, cut into cubes
    (3 matchboxes)
freshly ground black pepper

DRESSING:
15 ml (1 T) canola or olive oil
30 ml (2 T) vinegar
10 ml (2 t) sugar
1 ml (¼ t) salt
1 clove of garlic, crushed (½ teaspoon
    dry garlic)
5 ml (1 t) mustard
5 ml (1 t) fresh thyme, or
    2 ml (½ t) dried thyme
20 ml (4 t) freshly chopped parsley

1 Scrub the baby potatoes, but do NOT peel.
2 Place in a large saucepan, half cover with water and boil until cooked, but still firm. Drain and place in a dish to cool.
3 Meanwhile, wash and slice the green beans and boil until just cooked and still crisp. Drain and cool with the potatoes.
4 Add cherry tomatoes, cucumber and feta cheese. Toss lightly.
5 For the dressing: Mix all the ingredients together and pour over the salad ingredients. Mix gently, but thoroughly.
6 Chill in refrigerator for at least 1 hour.
7 Sprinkle with freshly ground black pepper to taste before serving.

This salad is a feast for the eye and the palate!

DIETICIAN'S NOTE:
● Although feta cheese is lower in fat (21 g fat per 100 g) than Cheddar cheese (33 g fat per 100 g), it is the main fat contributor in this salad. If you wish to lower the fat content, leave out or halve the feta cheese.
● Be generous with the parsley – it is full of anti-oxidants, which protect us from disease.
● Baby or new potatoes **with the skin** are lower in GI than mature potatoes, as they are firmer and have more skin in relation to the potato and are therefore digested more slowly. Take care not to overcook them.
● For **diabetics** this is the ideal salad for a braai as it contains less fat and has a lower GI than traditional potato salad.

NUTRIENTS PER SERVING
Glycaemic index 52 ● Fat 5 g
Carbohydrate 27 g ● Fibre 3 g
Protein 5 g ● kJ 731

ONE SERVING is equivalent to 2 STARCH and 1 FAT

Cabbage and apple salad, and Baby potato salad

GABI'S SALAD DRESSING
Makes 600 ml (20 x 30 ml portions)

1 vegetable stock cube or
   20 ml stock powder
400 ml boiling water
½ small onion, finely chopped
100 ml (⅖ cup) balsamic
   vinegar
1 ml (¼ t) crushed garlic
35 ml (7 t or 5 heaped t) sugar
10 ml (2 t) apple cider vinegar
1 ml (¼ t) salt
60 ml (4 T) olive oil

1 Place the crumbled stock cube and onion in a 1 litre measuring jug. Pour the boiling water over both and stir until the stock cube is completely dissolved.
2 Add the rest of the ingredients, except the olive oil, and stir well to mix thoroughly. Lastly, add the oil and stir again.
3 Store in a salad dressing bottle. Shake the bottle every time before pouring the dressing over salad.

This dressing can be kept out of the refrigerator for up to two weeks. Do not refrigerate this salad dressing as the oil will solidify and make it difficult to pour.
Because of the vinegar, salad dressings are best stored in glass bottles. Vinegar tends to 'dissolve' some plastics which means the dressing then becomes contaminated with plastic compounds.

NUTRIENTS PER SERVING
Glycaemic index 54 ● Fat 2.6 g
Carbohydrate 2 g ● Fibre –
Protein – ● kJ 136

ONE SERVING is equivalent to ½ FAT

DIETICIAN'S NOTE:
● The calculated GI of this dressing is rather high, but in practice it is much lower as it is consumed with the very low-GI tossed salad, therefore it really does not have much effect.
● Remember, sugar in this recipe is divided into 20 portions, that equals ¼ teaspoon sugar per person. So **diabetics**, don't panic.
● For a fat-free dressing, simply leave out the oil.

TOSSED SALAD or GREEK SALAD
Serves 6

TOSSED SALAD

GREEK SALAD

½ lettuce
2 tomatoes
¼ English cucumber
1 carrot
1 avocado
1 apple
lemon juice

1 Wash and break up the lettuce leaves and arrange on a platter.
2 Cut the tomatoes into quarters, and dice the cucumber. Place on top of lettuce.
3 Peel the carrot, then cut into matchsticks. Sprinkle on top of the other vegetables.
4 Peel the avocado, cut it into cubes and sprinkle it on top of the other vegetables.
5 Cut the apple into quarters, slice thinly and sprinkle with just enough lemon juice to prevent them turning brown. Add to the salad.
6 Serve with Gabi's salad dressing (*see* above) on the side.

NUTRIENTS PER SERVING

WITHOUT DRESSING

TOSSED SALAD
Glycaemic index <25 ● Fat 4 g
Carbohydrate 6 g ● Fibre 2 g
Protein 1 g ● kJ 267

ONE SERVING is equivalent to 1 FAT and FREE VEGETABLES

GREEK SALAD
Glycaemic index <25 ● Fat 8 g
Carbohydrate 7 g ● Fibre 2 g
Protein 4 g ● kJ 480

ONE SERVING is equivalent to ½ PROTEIN, 1 FAT and FREE VEGETABLES

DIETICIAN'S NOTE:
● For a **fat-free** salad, omit the avocado in the salad and the oil in the dressing.
● The high-GI carrot is a minor ingredient and goes well with all the other low-GI vegetables. Note that the GI is still <25!
● For a **Greek salad**, add 3 matchboxes of low-fat feta cheese, and 12 olives.
● The nutritional information given alongside is for the salad **without the dressing**. With the dressing the tossed salad will be **Jack Spratt Green**, and the Greek salad will be **Jack Spratt Orange**.

Gabi's salad dressing, and Greek salad

BEAN FRITTATA
Serves 6

5 ml (1 t) canola or olive oil
9 rashers lean bacon, all visible fat
  removed, chopped
1 onion, chopped
2 ml (½ t) crushed garlic
½ red pepper, chopped
1 x 410 g tin baked beans in tomato
  sauce
1 potato, cooked and diced
6 eggs
30 ml (2 T) water
salt and freshly ground black pepper
  to taste

NUTRIENTS PER SERVING
Glycaemic index 40 ● Fat 8 g
Carbohydrate 16 g ● Fibre 6 g
Protein 13 g ● kJ 794

ONE SERVING is equivalent to 1 STARCH
and 1½ PROTEIN

1 Fry the bacon, onion, garlic and red pepper in a frying pan with the oil and a little water until the onion is transparent. Add the beans and potato.
2 Beat together the eggs and water, and season to taste. Pour into the frying pan on top of the other ingredients and cook for 6–8 minutes. Lift the edge of the egg mixture as it sets to allow the runny egg to flow underneath it so as to cook all the egg into one big 'pancake'.
3 Place under the grill until golden brown on top, or cover with a lid for 3 minutes to cook the top of the frittata.
4 Sprinkle with parsley, cut into wedges and serve hot with Bran and oat loaf (page 28) or Healthy oat bread (page 32).

DIETICIAN'S NOTE:
● Serve this frittata, preceded by fresh fruit salad, for a delicious and balanced breakfast.
● Although potato has a high GI, in this recipe it makes up a small percentage, and is used together with lots of low-GI ingredients, which makes it quite acceptable.

MEXICAN BEAN SNACK
Serves 4

5 ml (1 t) canola or olive oil
1 onion, finely chopped
1 clove of garlic, crushed
½ green pepper, chopped
1 tomato, chopped
2 'lite' viennas
1 x 410 g tin of baked beans in
  tomato sauce
freshly ground black pepper to taste
5 ml (1 t) mild chilli or curry powder
100 g low-fat cheese, grated
  (3 matchboxes of cheese)
4 slices of hot toast

NUTRIENTS PER SERVING
Glycaemic index 53 ● Fat 10 g
Carbohydrate 43 g ● Fibre 10 g
Protein 19 g ● kJ 1378

ONE SERVING is equivalent to 2 STARCH
and 2 PROTEIN

1 Heat the oil and fry the onion, garlic and green pepper until soft. Add the tomato and simmer for another 3 minutes.
2 Add the rest of ingredients, except the cheese and toast, and cook for 5 minutes, stirring occasionally. Add some of the cheese and heat until the cheese has melted.
3 Pile generously onto the dry toast and sprinkle with the rest of the grated cheese. Serve hot.

An unusual and quick meal for Sunday nights or unexpected visitors.

DIETICIAN'S NOTE:
● For a balanced meal, serve fruit for dessert.
● Remember that bread, whether white or brown, has a high GI. But in this dish, by combining the bread with baked beans, the GI is lowered substantially.
● It is important to use 'lite' viennas, otherwise the fat content per portion goes up to 14 g.
● If only half the cheese is used, this dish will be **Jack Spratt Green Plus.**

HAMBURGER PATTIES WITH BBQ SAUCE

Serves 8

PATTIES
1 x 410 g tin brown or sugar beans, drained
15 ml (1 T) vinegar
15 ml (1 T) Worcestershire sauce
2 ml (½ t) crushed garlic
200 g lean topside mince
1 medium onion, chopped
1 stalk celery, chopped
1 slice bread, crumbed (brown or white)
250 ml (1 cup) oat bran
5 ml (1 t) instant beef stock powder
freshly ground black pepper
1 egg
8 hamburger rolls

BBQ SAUCE
1 onion, chopped
1 large apple, grated finely
1 ml (¼ t) crushed garlic
5 ml (1 t) canola or olive oil
60 ml (4 T) tomato sauce
1 tomato, chopped finely
125 ml (½ cup) water
20 ml (4 t) brown sugar
10 ml (2 t) Worcestershire sauce
5 ml (1 t) salt
10 ml (2 t) prepared mustard

NUTRIENTS PER HAMBURGER
Glycaemic index 57 ● Fat 7 g
Carbohydrate 53 g ● Fibre 7 g
Protein 16 g ● kJ 1454

ONE HAMBURGER WITH BBQ SAUCE is equivalent to 2 STARCH, 2 PROTEIN and 1 LIMITED VEGETABLE

1 For the patties, mash together the beans, vinegar, Worcestershire sauce and garlic, or process in a food processor.
2 Add the minced meat, chopped onion and celery, breadcrumbs, oat bran, beef stock powder, pepper and egg, and mix lightly to a firm consistency.
3 Form into 8 hamburger patties.
4 Lightly grease a frying pan with 5 ml (1 t) oil, ensuring that the oil is evenly spread all over the pan. Use an egglifter to spread the hot oil in the pan.
5 Fry the patties for 5 minutes on each side.
6 Serve on unbuttered hamburger rolls with tomato, lettuce and BBQ sauce.

BBQ SAUCE
1 Sauté onion, apple and garlic in the oil until transparent.
2 Add the rest of the ingredients and simmer for 5 minutes.
3 Serve on the hamburger patties.

These patties are very soft and do not have the 'meatiness' of normal hamburger patties. Liesbet and her family are quite happy to eat these hamburgers, but Gabi's family prefer to have normal meat patties. (See DIETICIAN'S NOTE *on how to do this and still have a low-GI meal.)*

DIETICIAN'S NOTE:
● Normally commercial bread rolls would not be allowed in this recipe as they have a very high GI. Because we have made the patties with half beans and half mince, and we have included a low-GI BBQ sauce, the effect of the high GI rolls is lessened.
● To keep the GI below 60, the bean and meat patties as well as the BBQ sauce must be eaten with the rolls.
● Brown and white rolls have a similar GI, although brown rolls contain slightly more fibre.
● For those who do not like the bean and meat patties, the alternative is to have a grilled lean-meat patty, on a hamburger bun made from the recipe for Breakfast oat baps (page 34).
● The BBQ sauce must be included to keep the GI low.
● Do NOT butter the rolls.
● These hamburgers make a **good carbo-loading** meal, especially if followed by a carbo-loading pudding (see Desserts, pages 106–113).

ALTERNATIVELY
● Use the recipe for Mini meatballs (page 96) for the hamburger patties, and use ordinary bread rolls. The GI of these patties plus a roll is also 57.
● Do NOT butter the rolls.
● Normal commercial hamburgers contain about 8 times the amount of fat, no fibre and the GI is very high. Most unhealthy!

FRENCH BREAD PIZZA

Serves 6. Serve with a large tossed salad for a quick and delicious light meal.

1 French bread (500 g)
½ x 410 g tin baked beans in
   tomato sauce
125 ml (½ cup) oat bran
5 ml (1 t) canola or olive oil
1 onion
¼ green pepper, chopped
5 ml (1 t) dried Italian herb mix
1ml (¼ t) dried crushed garlic
2 tomatoes
5 ml (1 t) mustard powder
8 rashers 'lite' bacon, all visible fat
   removed, chopped
250 ml (1 cup) grated low-fat
   mozzarella cheese (4 matchboxes)

NUTRIENTS PER SERVING

Glycaemic index 59 ● Fat 7 g
Carbohydrate 38 g ● Fibre 6 g
Protein 16 g ● kJ 1170

ONE SERVING is equivalent to 2 STARCH
and 2 PROTEIN

1 Preheat the oven to 180 °C.
2 Slice the French bread lengthwise and remove the inside from both halves. Discard 1 cup of the centre of the bread. Mix the leftover crumbed bread centre with beans and oat bran.
3 Heat the oil and gently fry the onion, green pepper, herbs and garlic. Add the tomatoes and cook until soft.
4 Mix the bread and beans with the onion and tomato mixture, and add the mustard. Pile the mixture into the bread halves. Sprinkle with bacon and, lastly, top with the cheese.
5 Place on a greased baking sheet and bake for 15 minutes.
6 Serve with a large tossed salad.

DIETICIAN'S NOTE:

● French bread has a high GI, therefore it is very important to remove some of the inside of the bread and replace it with the low-GI oat bran and beans.
● The GI of this pizza is still higher than we would like, but by using commercial French bread, it is impossible to get it lower.
● Anything made with flour as the main ingredient will have a high GI. This pizza version has a lower GI and lower fat content.
● All **takeaways** are therefore HIGH GI and HIGH fat.

BACON AND BROCCOLI QUICHE

Serves 8

BASE
250 ml (1cup) flour, sifted
   before measuring
125 ml (½ cup) oat bran
45 ml (3 T) 'lite' margarine
1 ml (¼ t) salt
1 egg
45 ml (3 T) ice water

FILLING
1 x 410 g tin small white beans, drained
250 ml (1 cup) broccoli florets, cut into
   small pieces
8 rashers lean bacon, chopped
1 large onion, finely chopped
3 eggs
100 ml (⅖ cup) skim milk
150 ml (⅗ cup) plain, low-fat yoghurt
salt and pepper to taste

NUTRIENTS PER SERVING

Glycaemic index 48 ● Fat 10 g
Carbohydrate 30 g ● Fibre 5 g
Protein 14 g ● kJ 1196

ONE SERVING is equivalent to 2 PROTEIN,
1½ STARCH, and 1 LIMITED VEGETABLE

2 ml (½ t) mustard powder
100 ml mozzarella cheese, grated (2 matchboxes)
5 ml (1 t) grated Parmesan cheese

1 For the base, rub together the flour, oat bran, margarine and salt until the mixture resembles bread crumbs.
2 Combine egg and water. Add 15 ml egg mixture at a time to the flour mixture and mix to a soft dough. Add more flour if it becomes sticky. Cover and chill for about 20 minutes.
3 Roll out and line a greased French flan dish or pie dish, or press the dough into the dish with your fingers.
4 For the filling, drain the beans and spread evenly over the base of the quiche. Sprinkle the broccoli evenly over the beans.
5 Fry the bacon and onion without adding any oil or other fat to the pan. If it catches, add a little water and stir.
6 Beat the eggs, milk and yoghurt together. Add the salt and mustard powder. Add the onion and bacon to the egg mixture, stir and pour over the quiche. Sprinkle with cheeses.
7 Bake at 180 °C for 25–30 minutes until the filling is firm.
8 Serve with a salad (*see Salads pages 46–55*).

DIETICIAN'S NOTE:

● Note: Even though we have used skim milk and low-fat yoghurt and no frying is involved, the fat is still 10 g per portion.
● **Quiches are very high in fat**, especially those that are commercially prepared.

Bacon and broccoli quiche, and French bread pizza

CHICKEN WITH CURRIED RICE

Serves 4

3 deboned chicken breasts, skinned
5 ml (1 t) canola or olive oil
1 large onion, finely chopped
1 stick celery, sliced
1 carrot, grated
6 sprigs fresh parsley, finely chopped
125 ml (½ cup) dry white wine
10 ml (2 t) tomato paste
125 ml (½ cup) prepared chicken stock
   (¼ stock cube or 5 ml stock powder)
freshly ground black pepper
1 bay leaf
20 g (¼ cup) grated Parmesan cheese

RICE
375 ml (1½ cups) water
125 g (¾ cups) basmati rice, uncooked
5 ml (1 t) 'lite' margarine
2 ml (½ t) salt
5 ml (1 t) curry powder

NUTRIENTS PER SERVING

Glycaemic index 48 ● Fat 7 g
Carbohydrate 27 g ● Fibre 2 g
Protein 29 g ● kJ 1333

ONE SERVING is equivalent to
1½ STARCH and 3 PROTEIN

1 Cut the chicken into 1 cm cubes.
2 Heat the oil in a saucepan or non-stick frying pan. Add the vegetables and parsley and stir-fry gently for about 10 minutes.
3 Add the chicken and cook, stirring for 4–5 minutes.
4 Stir in the combined tomato paste, wine and stock. Season with pepper and add the bay leaf.
5 Bring to a boil, reduce the heat and simmer gently for about 15 minutes. Remove the bay leaf before serving.
6 To cook the rice: add rice to the water in a saucepan and bring to a boil, simmer, half covered, for 18 to 20 minutes or until the water is absorbed.
7 Add the margarine, salt and curry powder. Stir until combined. Place the rice in a warmed serving dish, top with the chicken sauce and sprinkle with the Parmesan cheese. Serve with 2 or 3 cooked vegetables.

DIETICIAN'S NOTE:

● Carrots have a high GI, but with only 30 g per person and combined with other low-GI ingredients, they are quite safe.
● Parmesan cheese is high in saturated fat. In this recipe only 5 g per portion is used, and the flavour enhancement it gives is worth the little extra fat.

CHICKEN CASSEROLE

Serves 8. Bakes for 1½ hours

8 chicken thighs, ± 100 g each, skinned
1 onion, finely chopped
1 x 410 g tin of baked beans in
   tomato sauce
1 green pepper, chopped
12.5 ml (1 D) honey
2 ml (½ t) mustard powder
5 ml (1 t) mixed herbs
½ chicken stock cube or
   10 ml (2 t) chicken stock, dissolved in
200 ml (⅘ cup) boiled water
freshly ground black pepper to taste
4 rashers lean bacon (salt-reduced)
50 ml (4 D) chopped parsley

NUTRIENTS PER SERVING

Glycaemic index 47 ● Fat 7 g
Carbohydrate 13 g ● Fibre 4 g
Protein 21 g ● kJ 848

ONE SERVING is equivalent to
2½ PROTEIN

1 Arrange the chicken thighs in an oven dish. Mix the rest of the ingredients, except for the bacon and parsley, and spoon the mixture over the chicken thighs.
2 Cover and bake for 1 hour in a preheated oven at 180 °C, turning the chicken a few times.
3 Remove the cover and bake for another 30 minutes.
4 Remove all visible fat from the bacon and grill until crisp.
5 Mix the grilled bacon and the parsley and sprinkle over the chicken casserole.
6 Serve with basmati rice or durum wheat pasta, and vegetables.

This is a delicious, quick and easy casserole to prepare. Once in the oven, sit back and enjoy a drink while the chicken cooks itself.

DIETICIAN'S NOTE:

● Commercial honey has a very high GI, so only a little may be used in combination with lots of other low-GI ingredients.
● The portion size of this dish is ideal for women. Men may have 1½ portions. Remember to add 1 portion starch for each ½ cup portion cooked basmati rice or pasta.

Chicken with curried rice, and Chicken casserole

MALAYAN CHICKEN
Serves 4

4 chicken breasts, skin removed
5 ml (1 t) canola or olive oil
1 onion, chopped
1 x 410 g tin small white beans, drained
12.5 ml (1 D) cornflour
   (*see* DIETICIAN'S NOTE)
12.5 ml (1 D) curry powder
12.5 ml (1 D) 'lite' chutney or
   ordinary chutney
500 ml (2 cups) unsweetened
   orange juice
2 ml (½ t) salt
1 large green banana

1 Cut the chicken into cubes. Heat the oil in a frying pan, add the chicken and onion and brown.
2 Drain the beans and add, with the remaining ingredients – except the banana – to the chicken, and mix lightly. Spoon the mixture into a casserole dish and bake for 40 minutes in a preheated oven at 180 °C.
3 Add the sliced banana 10 minutes before serving.
4 Serve hot on basmati rice, cooked pearl barley or a mixture of the two, with 2 or 3 cooked vegetables.

This is a quick and easy dish for those rushed days when supper needs to be on the table in a hurry.

DIETICIAN'S NOTE:
● For **thickening sauces and gravies,** keep a jar with a mixture of half oat bran and half flour. This has a much lower GI than flour, cornflour or gravy powder which is normally used.
● Using chicken in a recipe always gives a higher protein content and helps to keep the fat content lower.
● The bonus of this dish is that it is also high in fibre, which is so often lacking in our meals today.
● Normally we discourage the use of cornflour for thickening sauces and gravies because of its high GI. But in this recipe the amount used is so little, and there are so many other low-GI ingredients, that it hardly has an effect on the GI.

NUTRIENTS PER SERVING
Glycaemic index 45 ● Fat 7 g
Carbohydrate 36 g ● Fibre 7 g
Protein 39 g ● kJ 1599

ONE SERVING is equivalent to 4 PROTEIN and 1½ FRUIT

CURRIED CHICKEN DISH
Serves 5

400 g sweet potato, cooked and cubed
500 g cooked chicken, deboned and
   skin removed

CURRY SAUCE
5 ml (1 t) canola or olive oil
1 large onion, finely chopped
5 ml (1 t) minced garlic
5–10 ml (1–2 t) curry powder, to taste
3 ml turmeric
5 ml (1 t) chicken spice
2 ml (½ t) salt
60 ml (4 T) brown grape vinegar
250 ml (1 cup) water
15 ml (1 T) apricot jam

1 First prepare the sauce by heating oil in a non-stick pan and gently frying the onion until golden brown. Add the garlic and spices, and stir well to combine.
2 Add the vinegar, water and apricot jam. Add the cooked sweet potato and 125 ml of the water they were cooked in. Add the cubed chicken and simmer for half an hour.
3 Slightly mash one third of the sweet potato, just enough to thicken the gravy.
4 Serve with basmati rice and sambals such as chopped onion and tomato, cucumber in natural low-fat yoghurt, and 'lite' chutney.

This pale yellow and mild chicken curry is easily and quickly prepared

DIETICIAN'S NOTE:
● The sweet potato gives the curry a rich flavour, and is lower in GI than ordinary potatoes.
● The GI of this meal is calculated without the sambals. If these are eaten, the GI would drop even further.
● Basmati rice is lower in GI than ordinary rice and is therefore the better choice for curry. If basmati rice is unavailable, use plain rice and add tinned lentils in a 1:1 ratio.

NUTRIENTS PER SERVING:
Glycaemic index 50 ● Fat 8 g
Carbohydrate 21 g ● Fibre 3 g
Protein 29 g ● kJ 1204

ONE SERVING is equivalent to 1 STARCH, 2½ PROTEIN and 1 LIMITED VEGETABLE

PASTA WITH BROCCOLI AND CHICKEN
Serves 4

5 ml (1 t) canola or olive oil
3 chicken breasts (about 150 g each),
   cut into thin strips
250 g tube pasta – penne, rigate or ziti
1 onion, sliced
1 red pepper, sliced into thin strips
5 ml (1 t) crushed garlic
1 x 410 g tin tomatoes, diced
½ chicken stock cube, dissolved in
250 ml (1 cup) boiling water
50 ml (4 D) sultanas
2 ml (½ t) grated orange rind
freshly ground black pepper
1000 ml (4 cups) small broccoli florets
5 ml (1 t) cornflour
10 ml (2 t) brown sugar
15 ml (1 T) balsamic vinegar (optional)

1 In a large non-stick frying pan, heat oil over medium heat until hot but not smoking. Add chicken and cook, stirring, until lightly browned. With a slotted spoon, transfer chicken to a plate.
2 Cook the pasta in lightly salted boiling water until just tender.
3 Meanwhile, add the onion, red pepper and garlic to the frying pan and cook, stirring, until the onion is transparent.
4 Add the tomatoes and their juice, stock, sultanas, orange rind and pepper and bring to the boil. Simmer until the sauce is slightly reduced.
5 Add the broccoli and cook until tender, about 5 minutes.
6 In a small bowl, combine the cornflour, sugar and vinegar. Return the chicken to the pan and stir in the cornflour mixture. Cook until the sauce is slightly thickened and the chicken is heated through. Toss the chicken with the hot, cooked pasta and serve with a salad.

This is a rather different, sweet and sour tomato pasta sauce. Freezing the chicken breasts for about 15 minutes will make it easier to slice them thinly.

DIETICIAN'S NOTE:
● Normally we discourage the use of cornflour for thickening sauces because of its high GI, but in this recipe very little is used and there are many other low-GI ingredients.

NUTRIENTS PER SERVING
Glycaemic index <30 ● Fat 6 g
Carbohydrate 55 g ● Fibre 8 g
Protein 36 g ● kJ 1772

ONE SERVING is equivalent to 3 STARCH and 3 PROTEIN

CHICKEN SPAGHETTI BOLOGNAISE
Serves 4

300 g durum wheat spaghetti
1 x 65 g pork sausage, casing removed
½ chicken stock cube or
   10 ml (2 t) stock powder
3 chicken breasts (about 150 g each),
   cut into 1 cm chunks
10 ml (2 t) crushed garlic
1 x 410 g tin whole tomatoes with juice,
   chopped
125 ml (½ cup) chopped parsley
freshly ground black pepper
10 ml (2 t) sugar
250 ml (1 cup) frozen peas or
   mange tout (snap peas)
60 g low-fat mozzarella cheese, grated
   (2 matchboxes)

1 Cook the spaghetti in lightly salted boiling water until tender but still firm.
2 Meanwhile, crumble the sausage meat into a large frying pan. Add a little water and cook over medium heat, stirring, until the sausage is no longer pink.
3 Add the stock powder, chicken and garlic. Cook, stirring, for about 4 minutes until the chicken is no longer pink.
4 Stir in the tomatoes with their juices, parsley, pepper and sugar and bring to the boil. Simmer for about 5 minutes.
5 Add the peas and cook until just heated through.
6 Toss the sauce with the hot pasta, sprinkle with mozzarella cheese and serve immediately with a salad.

This delicious pasta dish has the typical robust garlic and tomato flavour so common to Naples.

DIETICIAN'S NOTE:
● Whether you use the sugar or not, it does not raise the GI of the dish as so little is used.
● It is important to use pasta made from durum wheat as it has a much lower GI than pasta made from wheat flour.

NUTRIENTS PER SERVING
Glycaemic index 33 ● Fat 10 g
Carbohydrate 59 g ● Fibre 7 g
Protein 40 g ● kJ 2054

ONE SERVING is equivalent to 3 STARCH, 3 PROTEIN, and 1 LIMITED VEGETABLE

Pasta with broccoli and chicken, and Chicken spaghetti bolognaise

TAGLIATELLE WITH CHICKEN

Serves 4

5 ml (1 t) canola or olive oil
1 onion, finely diced
5 ml (1 t) minced garlic or
    2 ml (½ t) dried garlic flakes
3 chicken breasts, finely chopped
125 ml (½ cup) dry white wine
½ chicken stock cube dissolved in
180 ml (¾ cups) boiling water
250 g mushrooms, quartered (1 punnet)
1 x 410 g tin Italian tomatoes, chopped
7.5 ml (1½ t) sage, dried
1 small bay leaf
5 ml (1 t) sugar

freshly ground black pepper
250 g durum wheat tagliatelle
10 ml (2 t) finely grated Parmesan cheese

1 In a large non-stick frying pan heat the oil until hot but not smoking. Add the onion and garlic and cook, stirring, until the onions become transparent.
2 Add the chicken and cook, stirring to break up the meat, for about 5 minutes or until the chicken is no longer pink.
3 Add the wine and cook until almost evaporated and then add the stock, mushrooms, tomatoes with their juices, sage, bay leaf, sugar and pepper and bring to the boil.
4 Reduce heat to a simmer, cover and cook for about 20 minutes until the sauce is richly flavoured and thickened.
5 Meanwhile, cook the pasta until just tender. Drain well.
6 Toss the sauce with the hot pasta. Divide among four plates, sprinkle on Parmesan and serve with a salad.

DIETICIAN'S NOTE:

● Double the pasta for a good **carbo-loading** dish with 94 g sustained release carbohydrate, and limited fat and protein.

NUTRIENTS PER SERVING

Glycaemic index 33 ● Fat 6 g
Carbohydrate 50 g ● Fibre 4 g
Protein 34 g ● kJ 1714

ONE SERVING is equivalent to 3 STARCH, and 3 PROTEIN

CHICKEN STIR-FRY

Serves 6

5 ml (1 t) canola or olive oil
4 chicken breasts, cut into thin slices
2 onions, sliced
2 sticks celery, chopped
250 g (1 punnet) mushrooms, sliced
750 ml (3 cups) shredded cabbage
125 ml (½ cup) broccoli florets
125 ml (½ cup) cauliflower florets
1 large carrot, cut into julienne strips
1 green pepper, cut into strips
1 x 410g tin butter beans, drained

SAUCE
30 ml (2 T) reduced-salt soya sauce
25 ml (2 D) vinegar
15 ml (1 T) crushed garlic
5 ml (1 t) ground ginger
15 ml (1 T) sugar
20 ml (4 t) tomato sauce, ordinary or 'lite'
25 ml (2 D) cornflour
25 ml (2 D) oat bran
375 ml (1½ cups) water

1 Heat the oil in a wok or large frying pan. Gently stir-fry the onions until transparent.
2 Add the chicken and fry until browned, stirring all the time
3 Add all the shredded and chopped vegetables and stir-fry until just cooked. Add the butter beans and heat through.
4 For the sauce, mix all the ingredients and stir until lump free.
5 Pour the sauce over the stir-fry and stir well so that the sauce thickens evenly.
6 Serve with basmati rice or cooked pearl barley.

This stir-fry is also easy to do on a braai using a large, flat steel plate.

DIETICIAN'S NOTE:

● If basmati rice is unavailable, use ordinary white or brown rice mixed with tinned lentils. Use 250 ml uncooked rice with one 410 g tin of lentils. Cook the rice as usual and add the lentils at the end to just heat through.
● **Mushrooms** are not recommended for those suffering from gout.
● For a **carbo-loading** meal, leave out the chicken and have a double portion of stir-fry with lots of rice or barley. The stir-fry would then yield 27 g carbohydrate (901 kJ), and each 125 ml of rice or barley would yield another 28 g carbohydrate.
● Normally we discourage the use of **cornflour for thickening** sauces and gravies because of its high GI, but by combining **cornflour with oat bran** in a 1:1 ratio, the dumping of glucose in the blood is slowed down.

NUTRIENTS PER SERVING

Glycaemic index 35 ● Fat 5 g
Carbohydrate 20 g ● Fibre 7 g
Protein 29 g ● kJ 1075

ONE SERVING = 3 PROTEIN, 1 LIMITED VEGETABLE and FREE VEGETABLES

Tagliatelle with chicken, and Chicken stir-fry

MEXICAN FISH AND BEANS
Serves 4

5 ml (1 t) canola or olive oil
1 stick celery, finely diced
1 onion, finely chopped
5 ml (1 t) minced garlic
   (1 clove, crushed)
1 x 410 g tin of tomatoes,
   undrained and mashed
1 x 410 g tin of butter beans,
   well drained
5 ml (1 t) minced chilli
125 ml (½ cup) dry white wine
4 deboned white fish fillets (about 500 g),
   cut into cubes
30 ml (2 T) chopped fresh parsley
freshly ground black pepper

NUTRIENTS PER SERVING

WITH MASH/UNSIFTED MEALIE MEAL
Glycaemic index 50 ● Fat 8 g
Carbohydrate 37 g ● Fibre 8 g
Protein 31 g ● kJ 1640

ONE SERVING of fish and potato or 'pap' is equivalent to 2 STARCH and 3 PROTEIN

1 Heat the oil in a non-stick frying pan or saucepan.
2 Add the celery, onion and garlic and sauté for about 5 minutes or until soft.
3 Add the tomatoes, beans and chilli.
4 Simmer, uncovered, for 10 minutes.
5 Meanwhile, heat the wine in a medium-sized saucepan over moderate heat.
6 Add the fish, and poach gently for 3–4 minutes, or until just cooked through.
7 Combine the cooked fish and cooking juices with the tomato and bean mixture.
8 Add the parsley, and pepper to taste.
9 Serve immediately with mashed potato or 'pap' (stiff mealie meal porridge), and a mixed salad.

The mashed potatoes should be prepared using only low-fat or fat-free milk and very little 'lite' margarine.
The 'pap' should be made from unsifted mealie meal.
To thaw frozen fish steaks, place them in milk for that fresh-from-the-sea flavour.

DIETICIAN'S NOTE:

● This meal is a typical example of when a high-GI food, such as mashed potatoes, can successfully be combined with a low-GI dish containing legumes/beans. The GI of the fish and bean dish alone is 18, and the GI of mashed potatoes is 71. Together, the meal has a GI of 50.
● The nutrient analysis of the fish with the mashed potatoes or 'pap' is alongside.
● 'Pap' and mashed potatoes have similar GI values.
● It is interesting to note that if the mealie meal porridge ('pap') is cooked a few hours ahead and allowed to cool and is then reheated when the fish is ready to eat, the GI of the 'pap' is lowered by at least 10 points.
● We recommend that if time allows, you make the porridge beforehand and allow it to cool. Reheat it just before serving.
● This dish may also be served with basmati rice. If basmati rice is not available, use ordinary rice and add ready-cooked, tinned lentils in a 1:1 ratio. Drain the lentils, add to the hot rice and gently reheat.

FISH CAKES

Makes 6 large fish cakes or 12 small fish cakes. A quick and easy dish that is also easy on the pocket.

1 x 410 g tin salmon or pilchards
   in tomato sauce
1 onion, finely grated
10 ml (2 t) finely chopped parsley
250 ml (1 cup) oats
1 egg
15 ml (1 T) or less canola or olive oil

NUTRIENTS PER LARGE FISH CAKE

Glycaemic index 27 ● Fat 7 g
Carbohydrate 3 g ● Fibre 0.5 g
Protein 14 g ● kJ 565

ONE LARGE FISH CAKE (patty) is equivalent to 2 PROTEIN

1 Remove sauce from the fish and flake the fish. Add the onion, parsley and oats.
2 Mix with the egg and some of the sauce from the fish to make a firm mixture. Be careful not to overmix.
3 Shape the mixture into 6 large or 12 small fish cakes or patties.
4 Heat the oil and fry quickly.
5 Serve with baby (new) jacket potatoes sprinkled with parsley and 2 to 3 cooked vegetables, or with a large mixed salad.

DIETICIAN'S NOTE:

● Use this recipe for fish burger patties. Because the GI of the patties is so low, they can be eaten with an ordinary bread roll!
● Remember not to 'butter' the roll to keep the fat content down. Tomato sauce, mustard and/or 'lite' chutney can be added.
● Pilchards are a rich source of Ω-3 (omega-3) essential fatty acids. Modern diets are usually lacking in Ω-3 fatty acids so this is a pleasant way to include such a rich source once a week. Ω-3 fatty acids are especially important for allergy-prone people and those with compromised immune systems. Ω-3 fatty acids are also shown to be beneficial in ADHD and heart disease.

COUNTRY-STYLE TUNA BAKE

Serves 4

125 g durum wheat screw noodles
5 ml (1 t) canola or olive oil
1 onion, chopped
125 g sliced mushrooms (½ punnet)
15 ml (1 T) flour
15 ml (1 T) tomato puree
125 ml (½ cup) low-fat milk
pinch of dried basil
1 ml (¼ t) salt
freshly ground black pepper
60 g low-fat Cheddar cheese, grated
   (2 matchboxes)
1 tin tuna in brine, drained
10 ml (2 t) grated Parmesan cheese

NUTRIENTS PER SERVING

Glycaemic index 33 ● Fat 8 g
Carbohydrate 28 g ● Fibre 2 g
Protein 18 g ● kJ 1071

One serving is equivalent to 1 STARCH, 2 PROTEIN and FREE VEGETABLES

1 Preheat the oven to 150 °C.
2 Cook the pasta in plenty of boiling, lightly salted water until just tender. Drain and set aside.
3 Heat the oil and sauté the onions and mushrooms.
4 Blend in the flour and add the tomato puree.
5 Mix in the milk, basil, salt and pepper. Continue stirring until the mixture thickens.
6 Combine with the cooked pasta, cheese and tuna.
7 Pour the mixture into an ovenproof dish and sprinkle with the Parmesan cheese.
8 Bake in a preheated oven for 25–30 minutes.
9 Serve with a large mixed salad.

This is a quick and easy fish pie.

DIETICIAN'S NOTE:

● By doubling up the noodles, this is a delicious **carbo-loading** meal. The carbohydrate content would go up to 50 g per portion, but the protein, fat and GI would remain las ow as they are.
● Normally we do not recommend flour for thickening of sauces as it has a high GI. But in this recipe, the low-GI milk and pasta offset the small amount of flour used.
● The higher fat content of this fish dish, despite using so little tuna in brine, is due to the inclusion of milk and cheese. It can be lowered slightly by using skim milk.

Country-style tuna bake, and Fish cakes

CURRIED FISH AND RICE
Serves 6

400 g frozen hake fillets
5 ml (1 t) fish spice
250 ml (1 cup) low-fat milk
1 medium onion, chopped
5 ml (1 t) canola or olive oil
5–7 ml (1–1½ t) curry powder
1 ml turmeric
125 ml (½ cup) basmati rice, uncooked
2 ml (½ t) salt
2 hard-boiled eggs
rind and juice of 1 lemon
1 x 410 g tin brown lentils
125 ml (½ cup) low-fat yoghurt
2 ml (½ t) lemon pepper

NUTRIENTS PER SERVING
Glycaemic index 41 ● Fat 5 g
Carbohydrate 26 g ● Fibre 4 g
Protein 21 g ● kJ 1035

ONE SERVING is equivalent to 1 STARCH,
2 PROTEIN

1 Skin the fish fillets and put them in a saucepan. Sprinkle with the fish spice. Pour milk over, cover and cook for 10 minutes.
2 Drain, retaining the cooking juices. Add enough water to the cooking juices to make 600 ml.
3 Flake the fish removing the fish bones.
4 Fry the onion in the oil until soft. Add the curry powder and turmeric. Add the rice, salt and milk and water mixture. Stir well. Simmer for 20 minutes or until the rice is done.
5 Meanwhile, shell the eggs and cut into wedges.
6 Add the eggs, fish, lentils, lemon rind and juice to the rice mixture. Mix lightly, and gently heat through.
7 Add the yoghurt, mix and heat for a few seconds. (Be careful – if the dish gets too hot the yoghurt will curdle).
8 Sprinkle with lemon pepper and serve hot or cold with salad or cooked vegetables.

DIETICIAN'S NOTE:

● All fish dishes have a low fat content, as fish is a very lean source of protein.

BEAN CASSEROLE WITH PIZZA TOPPING
Serves 4

5 ml (1 t) oil
2 onions, chopped
2 green peppers, chopped
410 g tin brown or sugar beans
250 ml (1 cup) cooked, brown rice
60 ml (4 T) chopped parsley
2 thin slices fresh brown bread, crumbed
2 eggs (one whole egg + 1 egg white)
125 ml (½ cup) plain, low-fat yoghurt
salt and black pepper
3 tomatoes, thinly sliced
60 g mozzarella cheese, grated
   (2 matchboxes)
30 ml (2 T) grated Parmesan cheese
2 ml (½ t) dried origanum
1 ml (¼ t) dried basil
5 ml (1 t) olive oil

NUTRIENTS PER SERVING
Glycaemic index 36 ● Fat 9 g
Carbohydrate 42 g ● Fibre 10 g
Protein 17 g ● kJ 1406

ONE PORTION is equivalent to 3 STARCH
and 2 PROTEIN

1 Preheat the oven to 180 °C.
2 Heat the oil and sauté the onion and green pepper until soft. Set aside.
3 Drain the beans and mix with the rice, parsley, bread crumbs, onions and green pepper.
4 Beat the egg and yoghurt together and season.
5 Add the bean mixture. Mix well.
6 Spoon into a greased ovenproof dish and spread evenly.
7 Cover with tomato slices and mixed grated cheeses.
8 Sprinkle with the herbs and, lastly, with olive oil.
9 Bake for 25 minutes at 180 °C until the cheese bubbles.

DIETICIAN'S NOTE:

● **Vegetarian dishes** are often perceived to be-low fat owing to the lack of meat, fish or chicken. They are, in fact, usually very **high in fat**. This dish only has such a low fat content because we have limited the oil and cheese to a minimum.
● This dish makes a **good carbo-loading** meal. It is high in slowly absorbed carbohydrates and both the fat and the protein are not too high.
● Bread and rice are both high-GI ingredients which have been offset by all the other low-GI ingredients
● This dish contains both egg and dairy, therefore it is suitable for **lacto-ovo vegetarians**.

VEGETABLE LASAGNE
Serves 6

1 bunch spinach, washed and stalks
  removed (500 g)
200 g instant durum wheat
  lasagne sheets
10 ml (2 t) grated Parmesan cheese
125 ml (½ cup) grated, low-fat
  mozzarella cheese (2 matchboxes)

VEGETABLE SAUCE
5 ml (1 t) canola or olive oil
2 onions, chopped
10 ml (2 t) minced garlic
250 g (1 punnet) mushrooms, sliced
½ small green pepper, chopped
1 x 410 g tin mixed beans, drained
1 x 410 g tin tomatoes with juice,
  mashed
5 ml (1 t) dried mixed herbs

CHEESE SAUCE
5 ml (1 t) 'lite' margarine
20 ml (4 t) flour
375 ml (1½ cups) low-fat milk
60 g low-fat cheese (2 matchboxes)
pinch of ground nutmeg
2 ml (½ t) salt
freshly ground black pepper to taste

1 Lightly steam the spinach until just wilted, then drain well
2 For the vegetable sauce, heat the oil in a non-stick frying pan. Add the onions and garlic and cook for about 5 minutes.
3 Add the mushrooms and green pepper and cook for a further 3 minutes. Add the beans, tomatoes and herbs. Simmer for 15 minutes.
4 For the cheese sauce, melt the margarine, and stir in the milk.
5 In a 500 ml glass bowl or jug, mix the flour with 50 ml water to a smooth paste. Remove the hot milk from the heat and gradually add the milk, 50 ml at a time, to the flour paste, stirring after each addition until smooth. Pour the sauce back into the saucepan.
6 Return to heat and stir until sauce is smooth and thickened. Remove from heat and stir in cheese, nutmeg, salt and pepper.
7 To assemble, pour half the vegetable sauce over the base of a lasagne dish. Cover with a layer of lasagne sheets, then half the spinach. Spread half the cheese sauce over the spinach. Top with remaining vegetable sauce and lasagne sheets. Cover with remaining spinach and finish with the remaining cheese sauce. Sprinkle with Parmesan and mozzarella cheese.
8 Bake in a preheated oven at 180 °C for 45 minutes to 1 hour until bubbly and brown.

Although this recipe looks quite long, it is in fact very easy to prepare and well worth the effort. It is quite delicious for a vegetarian meal.
To soften the lasagne sheets and prevent them from curling up, dip each sheet in hot water as you assemble the dish.

DIETICIAN'S NOTE:
● This dish has an exceptionally high fibre content and is also very low in fat.
● Spinach has not been tested to date, but we suspect that it has a high GI, since marogo has a high GI and is similar to spinach. In this recipe it is combined with so many other low-GI vegetables, that the GI of the whole dish still remains low.
● It is important to use durum wheat pasta as it has a low GI.

NUTRIENTS PER SERVING
Glycaemic index <32 ● Fat 7 g
Carbohydrate 44 g ● Fibre 11 g
Protein 19 g ● kJ 1367

ONE SERVING is equivalent to 2 STARCH,
2 PROTEIN and 1 LIMITED VEGETABLE

WHY DO WE ADD DRY BEANS (LEGUMES) TO SO MANY DISHES?

Most of us do not know how to use legumes anymore. To help you see how easy it is to include them in everyday meals, we have added them in tasty and easy ways to many of our recipes.
Beans (and all legumes) have many health advantages:
● Legumes actively bind cholesterol.
● Legumes can lower morning blood glucose readings in diabetics.
● Legumes are rich in soluble and insoluble fibre and thereby help in Irritable Bowel Syndrome.
● Legumes are very effective in lowering the GI of any meal.
● Legumes increase the satiety value of meals, and are therefore effective in slimming diets.
● The soluble fibre in legumes stimulates the immune system in the bowel.
● Legumes are a quick and easy way to increase the fibre content of any meal.
● Legumes are low in fat, a definite advantage in our age of high-fat fast foods.
● Legumes are an inexpensive source of protein.

VEGETABLE CURRY

Serves 6

5 ml (1 t) canola or olive oil
1 medium onion, chopped
10 ml (2 t) minced garlic
25 ml (2 D) minced ginger
10 ml (2 t) ground cumin
10 ml (2 t) ground coriander
10 ml (2 t) turmeric
10 ml (2 t) curry powder
2 ml (½ t) minced chilli, optional
3 ml (½ t) salt
125 ml (½ cup) water
1 large potato, unpeeled, cut into cubes
500 ml (2 cups) cubed pumpkin
250 ml (1 cup) cauliflower florets
1 x 410 g tin tomatoes with juices,
　chopped
1 x 410 g tin chickpeas, drained
1 red pepper, thickly sliced
4 baby marrows (zucchini), thickly sliced

CREAMY SAUCE
5 ml (1 t) 'lite' margarine
½ chicken stock cube, dissolved in
250 ml (1 cup) boiling water
125 ml (½ cup) low-fat evaporated milk,
　e.g. Nestlé Lite
20 ml (4 t) flour

NUTRIENTS PER SERVING

Glycaemic index　37 ● Fat　4 g
Carbohydrate　25 g ● Fibre　7 g
Protein　8 g ● kJ　753

ONE SERVING is equivalent to 1 STARCH,
1 PROTEIN and FREE VEGETABLES

1　Heat the oil in a large saucepan, add the onion and garlic and gently fry until soft. Add the spices and cook for 1 minute.

2　Add the water, potato, pumpkin, cauliflower, tomatoes and chickpeas. Simmer for 20 minutes.

3　Add the sliced red pepper and baby marrows and simmer for another 10 minutes.

4　Meanwhile, prepare the creamy chicken sauce. Melt margarine in a small saucepan. When hot, add the stock, water and milk.

5　In a glass bowl, mix the flour with 50 ml water to a smooth paste. When the milk and stock is hot, pour half of it onto the flour paste and stir well.

6　Pour the flour and milk mixture back into the saucepan with the other half of the milk and stock and bring to the boil, stirring until thick and creamy.

7　Add the sauce to the curried vegetables and mix gently.

8　Serve on basmati rice.

DIETICIAN'S NOTE:

● Normally one would expect a vegetable curry to have only vegetable portions. However, the creamy sauce and chickpeas both contribute appreciable amounts of protein. The chickpeas, potato and vegetables contribute starch, so this vegetarian dish can be counted as protein and starch with free vegetables.

● Also take note that we have skimped on the amount of oil and 'lite' margarine used, and insisted on low-fat evaporated milk to keep the fat content of the dish low. Most vegetarian dishes are high in fat despite the fact that no meat, fish or chicken is used. It is important to use the chickpeas, otherwise the GI of the dish may be raised too much due to the use of the potato and pumpkin.

BEAN AND NOODLE CASSEROLE
Serves 4

5 ml (1 t) canola or olive oil
1 onion, chopped
2 cloves garlic, crushed
1 tomato, chopped
1 x 410 g tin baked beans in tomato
    sauce
5 ml (1 t) origanum
5 ml (1 t) basil
250 ml (1 tub) fat-free cottage cheese
100 g mozzarella cheese, grated and
    divided in two (3 matchboxes)
250 g mushrooms (1 punnet), sliced
1 egg, beaten
4 x 250 ml (4 cups) cooked durum
    wheat noodles (2 cups when raw)

NUTRIENTS PER SERVING
Glycaemic index 35 ● Fat 10 g
Carbohydrate 61 g ● Fibre 11 g
Protein 26 g ● kJ 1808

ONE SERVING is equivalent to 3 STARCH
and 3 PROTEIN

1. Preheat the oven to 180 °C.
2. Heat the oil, add the onion and garlic and sauté until soft.
3. Add the tomato, herbs and beans and bring to the boil.
4. Lower the heat and simmer, uncovered, for 10 minutes.
5. Mix the cottage cheese, half the mozzarella cheese, the mushrooms and egg well.
6. Grease an ovenproof dish, put one half of the noodles into it, top it with half of the cheese mixture and end with half of the bean mixture.
7. Repeat the layers and sprinkle the remaining cheese on top.
8. Bake for 45 minutes in a preheated oven at 180 °C.
9. Serve hot with a green salad or two cooked vegetables.

DIETICIAN'S NOTE:
● It is important to use fat-free cottage cheese, as the mozzarella already pushes up the fat content.
● The exceptionally high fibre content compensates for the relatively high fat content, therefore it is **Jack Spratt Green Plus.**
● Vegetarian dishes are usually very high in fat because oil, milk, eggs and cheese are used in abundance.
● This dish is suitable for **carbo-loading**. It is rich in slow-release carbohydrates and the fat and protein are not too high.

POTATO AND BEAN PIE
Serves 6

2 x 410 g tin brown beans or mixed
    beans, drained
1 carrot, sliced
1 tomato, diced
250 ml (1 cup) cabbage, finely shredded
125 ml (½ cup) green beans, chopped
125 ml (½ cup) baby marrows, sliced
1 onion, chopped
1 clove garlic, crushed, or
    2 ml (½ t) dried garlic flakes
5 ml (1 t) dried mixed herbs
freshly ground black pepper to taste
½ beef or vegetable stock cube,
    dissolved in
250 ml (1 cup) boiling water
25 ml (5 t) cornflour
30 ml (2 T) BBQ sauce (page 58)
18 new (baby) potatoes, cooked
20 ml (4 t) 'lite' margarine, melted

NUTRIENTS PER SERVING
Glycaemic index 46 ● Fat 3 g
Carbohydrate 37 g ● Fibre 10 g
Protein 10 g ● kJ 1052.3

ONE SERVING is equivalent to 2 STARCH,
1 PROTEIN and 1 LIMITED VEGETABLE

1. Preheat the oven to 180 °C.
2. Combine the beans, vegetables and seasoning and place the mixture in an ovenproof dish.
3. Mix the cornflour into the stock and pour the beef stock and BBQ sauce over the vegetables and beans.
4. Slice the potatoes and arrange the slices in a layer on top of the bean mixture. Pour the margarine over evenly so all the potatoes are greased.
5. Cover and bake for 45 minutes at 180 °C.
6. Remove the lid and bake for another 15 minutes to brown the potatoes.
7. Serve hot with a green salad to make a complete meal.

DIETICIAN'S NOTE:
● As a rule we do not advocate the use of cornflour for thickening gravies. But in this recipe, so little is used among so many other low-GI ingredients, that it has little effect on the GI.
● This makes a good **carbo-loading** meal. The carbohydrate is slowly released and plentiful with not too much protein and fat.
● This dish has a high fibre and a very low fat content, that is why it is classified as **Jack Spratt Green Plus.**

CHEESE SOUFFLÉ
Serves 4

1 x 410 g tin baked beans in
   tomato sauce
100 ml (⅖ cup) oat bran
250 ml (1 cup) fresh bread crumbs
   (2 slices bread)
3 eggs (1 whole egg + 2 egg whites)
100 ml (⅖ cup) skim milk
2 ml crushed garlic
5 ml (1 t) mixed herbs, dried
salt and freshly ground black pepper to
   taste
60 g low-fat mozzarella cheese, grated
   (2 matchboxes)
30 g low-fat Cheddar cheese, grated
   (1 matchbox)
125 ml (½ cup) finely chopped parsley

NUTRIENTS PER SERVING
Glycaemic index 51 ● Fat 8 g
Carbohydrate 30 g ● Fibre 9 g
Protein 16 g ● kJ 1066

ONE SERVING is equivalent to 2 STARCH
and 2 PROTEIN

1 Preheat the oven to 180 °C.
2 Mash the beans with a fork or process in a food processor or liquidizer until smooth, but not for longer than 1 minute.
3 Beat together the beans, oat bran, fresh bread crumbs, egg yolk, milk, crushed garlic and herbs until fairly smooth. Do not overmix.
4 Season with salt and pepper.
5 Mix the grated cheeses and parsley and fold two thirds of the cheeses into the soufflé mix.
6 Whisk the egg whites until stiff peaks form and gently fold under bean mixture. Pour into a greased 16 cm ovenproof soufflé dish and bake for 30 minutes.
7 Sprinkle with the remaining grated cheese and parsley and bake for a further 5 minutes or until the cheese has melted.
8 Serve immediately with a large tossed salad (see Salads, pages 46–55).

This is the ultimate way to disguise baked beans! If you don't tell anybody, no one will even guess that the soufflé contains baked beans. An easy soufflé that does not collapse when taken out of the oven.

DIETICIAN'S NOTE:
● Traditional soufflés are high in fat without any fibre at all.
● This version is much lower in fat and has an incredible fibre content. It is, therefore, very important that you use **only one egg yolk** and **skim milk**.

SAVOURY BEAN BAKE
Serves 4

5 ml (1 t) canola or olive oil
1 onion, chopped
2 x 410 g tins baked beans
   in tomato sauce
2 hard-boiled eggs, chopped
30 ml (2 T) parsley, chopped
2 ml (½ t) salt
freshly ground black pepper
2 ml (½ t) dried marjoram
3 tomatoes, sliced
1 slice brown bread, crumbed
90 g low-fat mozzarella cheese, grated
   (3 matchboxes)

NUTRIENTS PER SERVING
Glycaemic index 45 ● Fat 10 g
Carbohydrate 46 g ● Fibre 18 g
Protein 19 g ● kJ 1463

ONE SERVING is equivalent to
2½ STARCH and 2½ PROTEIN

1 Heat the oil and sauté the onion until done.
2 Add the beans, eggs, parsley, salt, pepper and marjoram.
3 Turn into a greased ovenproof dish.
4 Garnish with the sliced tomatoes, grated mozzarella and crumbed bread, and place under a hot grill for 5–10 minutes until crisp and golden brown.

This is a very easy and delicious vegetarian main dish. Serve with a large salad or 2 cooked vegetables.

DIETICIAN'S NOTE:
● Vegetarian dishes are usually very high-fat dishes despite the fact that they do not contain any meat, fish or chicken. Only because the oil and the cheese are so limited in this dish, does it qualify as low-fat.
● This dish has an exceptionally high fibre content, and as the fat is <3g/100 g, it is classified as **Jack Spratt Green Plus.**

Cheese soufflé, and Savoury bean bake

SPAGHETTI AND BEAN BOLOGNAISE
Serves 4

250 g uncooked durum wheat spaghetti
5 ml (1 t) canola or olive oil
2 rashers lean bacon, chopped
2 medium onions, chopped
5 ml (1 t) crushed garlic or 2 cloves garlic
1 carrot, peeled and grated coarsely
1 green pepper, chopped
4 tomatoes, peeled and diced
10 ml (2 t) thyme
10 ml (2 t) origanum
10 ml (2 t) basil
2 ml (½ t) salt
freshly ground black pepper to taste
1 x 410 g tin brown beans, drained
½ x 410 g tin small white beans, drained
1 x 65 g tin tomato paste
20 ml (4 t) Parmesan cheese

1 Cook the spaghetti in lightly salted water until done.
2 Heat the oil in a large saucepan, and gently fry the bacon, onion, garlic, carrot, and green pepper until the onion is transparent. If it catches add 15–30 ml water and stir.
3 Add the diced tomatoes and simmer for 5 minutes
4 Add herbs, salt, pepper, beans and tomato paste and simmer for a further 5 minutes
5 Lightly mix the cooked spaghetti into the bean and tomato mixture, if desired.
6 Spoon onto a serving dish and sprinkle with Parmesan cheese.
7 Serve immediately with either two cooked vegetables or a tossed salad.

DIETICIAN'S NOTE:
● This meal is ideal for **carbo-loading** as it contains plenty of long-acting carbohydrates with not too much fat and protein.
● This dish has a high fibre content, and as the fat is <3g/100 g, it is classified as **Jack Spratt Green Plus.**

NUTRIENTS PER SERVING
Glycaemic index 31 ● Fat 5 g
Carbohydrate 72 g ● Fibre 14 g
Protein 20 g ● kJ 1779

ONE SERVING is equivalent to
4 STARCH and 2 PROTEIN

FETTUCCINE WITH MUSHROOMS
Serves 4

5 ml (1 t) canola or olive oil
12 rashers lean bacon, visible fat removed
    and thinly sliced
150 g (3 cups) uncooked fettuccine pasta
100 g small mushrooms, sliced or
    1 x 200 g tin mushrooms, drained
2 ml (½ t) crushed garlic
5 ml (1 t) wholegrain mustard
30 ml (2 T) red or white wine, optional
15 ml (1 T) cornflour
25 ml (2 D) water
250 ml (1 cup) low-fat milk
freshly ground black pepper
30 g low-fat Cheddar cheese, grated
    (1 matchbox of cheese)
10 ml (2 t) Parmesan cheese, to serve

1 Heat the oil in a non-stick saucepan and cook the sliced bacon until browned.
2 Meanwhile, in a large saucepan of boiling water with 1 ml of salt, boil the fettuccine, uncovered, until just tender. Drain.
3 Add the mushrooms and garlic to the bacon and cook for 2 minutes, or until the mushrooms are cooked.
4 Stir in the mustard and wine and cook a further 3 minutes.
5 Mix the cornflour and water to a smooth paste, add to the sauce and stir over low heat until the mixture becomes a thick paste. Remove from the heat and gradually add the milk and pepper, stirring with a whisk until well combined. Return to heat and cook until the sauce is thick and creamy.
6 Pour the sauce over the pasta, sprinkle with grated cheeses and serve immediately with a salad to complete the meal.

This is a tasty low-fat version of the usual pasta dish with the creamy sauce you get in restaurants.

DIETICIAN'S NOTE:
● Cornflour has a very high GI and we usually try to leave it out or use oat bran instead. In this dish there are so many other low-GI ingredients, and so little cornflour is used, that it is quite safe.

NUTRIENTS PER SERVING
Glycaemic index 35 ● Fat 9 g
Carbohydrate 33 g ● Fibre 2 g
Protein 16 g ● kJ 1139

ONE SERVING is equivalent to 2 STARCH
and 2 PROTEIN

Spaghetti and bean bolognaise, and Fettuccine with mushrooms

MACARONI WITH MUSHROOM SAUCE
Serves 4

250 g (3 cups) durum wheat macaroni
1 ml (¼ t) salt

SAUCE
5 ml (1 t) olive oil
1 medium onion, finely sliced
5 ml (1 t) minced garlic (1 clove, crushed)
500 g (2 punnets) mushrooms
5 ml (1 t) paprika
10 ml (2 t) Dijon mustard
30 ml (2 T) tomato paste
15 ml (1 T) flour
250 ml (1 cup) low-fat evaporated milk
30 g low-fat Cheddar cheese, grated
   (1 matchbox)
4 chopped spring onions
freshly ground black pepper
30 ml (2 T) freshly chopped parsley
20 ml (4 t) grated Parmesan cheese

1 In a large saucepan, cook the pasta, uncovered, in boiling water with 1 ml salt until just tender. Drain and keep warm.
2 Meanwhile, prepare the sauce. Heat the oil in a non-stick frying pan, add the onion, garlic and mushrooms and cook for about 5 minutes or until softened.
3 Combine the paprika, mustard, tomato paste, flour and milk in a small jug. Stir into mushroom mixture with the cheese and cook over low heat, stirring frequently, for 5 minutes.
4 Add the spring onions and pepper to taste.
5 Pour the sauce over the pasta and toss gently to combine.
6 Serve sprinkled with parsley and Parmesan cheese.

This dish is quick and easy to put together for a hasty supper. Add a tossed salad, and the meal is complete.

DIETICIAN'S NOTE:
● Parsley is rich in antioxidant vitamins which protect us from disease, so be generous and use lots.
● For **carbo-loading** use one and half times the amount of pasta with the same amount of sauce. This gives a carbohydrate value of 85 g per portion with a GI of 40. The energy value goes up to 2126 kJ per portion.
● Always use pasta made from durum wheat – pasta made from ordinary wheat flour has a much higher GI.

NUTRIENTS PER SERVING
Glycaemic index 38 ● Fat 7 g
Carbohydrate 60 g ● Fibre 5 g
Protein 18 g ● kJ 1548

ONE SERVING is equivalent to
3 STARCH and 2 PROTEIN/DAIRY

CREAMY VEGETARIAN PASTA
Serves 4

250 g (3 cups) durum wheat pasta shells
5 ml (1 t) canola or olive oil
½ onion, finely chopped
2 carrots, cut into 1 cm cubes
250 ml (1 cup) snap peas (mange tout)
500 ml (2 cups) cherry tomatoes, halved
3 ml (½ t) dried thyme
salt and freshly ground black pepper
1 x 410 g tin salad cuts asparagus
   (use the water as well)
10 ml (2 t) cornflour mixed with
20 ml (4 t) water
60 ml (4 T) fat-reduced cream

1 Cook pasta in lightly salted water until just tender. Drain well.
2 Meanwhile, in a large non-stick frying pan, heat the oil until hot, but not smoking, over medium heat. Add the onion and carrots and cook until the carrots are softened.
3 Add the snap peas and cook gently for 1 minute.
4 Add tomatoes, thyme, a pinch of salt, and pepper. Increase the heat and cook on high until the tomatoes are soft.
5 Add asparagus and its water and bring to the boil. Add the cornflour mixture and cook, stirring until the sauce thickens.
6 Stir in the cream until well blended.
7 Toss the sauce and the hot pasta together and serve.

A lovely light cream sauce that lets the vegetables shine through.

DIETICIAN'S NOTE:
● Asparagus is not suitable for persons suffering from gout.
● It is important to use fat-reduced cream in this dish to keep the fat content low. It is available from Woolworths.
● This dish is suitable for **carbo-loading** as it contains lots of long-acting carbohydrate with very little fat and protein.

NUTRIENTS PER SERVING
Glycaemic index 35 ● Fat 4 g
Carbohydrate 53 g ● Fibre 6 g
Protein 10 g ● kJ 1201

ONE SERVING is equivalent to 3 STARCH
and 1 PROTEIN

Creamy vegetarian pasta, and Macaroni with mushroom sauce

BOBOTIE
Serves 6

5 ml (1 t) oil
2 onions, sliced
2 cloves of garlic, crushed, or
    5 ml (1 t) crushed garlic or flakes
500 g topside mince
25 ml curry powder – may seem a lot,
    but the lentils suck up all the flavour
2 ml (½ t) salt
30 ml (2 T) 'lite' or ordinary chutney
15 ml (1 T) smooth apricot jam
15 ml (1 T) Worcestershire sauce
5 ml (1 t) turmeric
30 ml (2 T) brown vinegar
25 g (4 T) oat bran
1 x 410 g tin brown lentils
100 ml (⅖ cup) sultanas
2 eggs, beaten separately
250 ml (1 cup) low-fat milk
pinch of salt and turmeric
bay leaves or fresh citrus leaves

NUTRIENTS PER SERVING

Glycaemic index 27 ● Fat 10 g
Carbohydrate 17 g ● Fibre 4 g
Protein 26 g ● kJ 1170

ONE SERVING is equivalent to 3 PROTEIN
and 1 FRUIT/LIMITED VEGETABLE

1 Preheat the oven to 180 °C.
2 Heat the oil in a saucepan and fry the onion and garlic until soft. Add the meat and fry until brown.
3 Add the curry powder, salt, chutney, apricot jam, Worcestershire sauce, turmeric and vinegar to the meat and onion mixture. Mix well.
4 Add the oat bran, lentils and sultanas to the meat and simmer for a few minutes. Remove from the heat.
5 Add one egg, mix well and spoon into a greased ovenproof dish. Level the mixture.
6 Beat the other egg with the milk, salt and turmeric.
7 Pour egg and milk over the meat, put bay leaves on top and bake in the preheated oven for one hour.
8 Serve with basmati rice and a large salad.

DIETICIAN'S NOTE:

● As soon as red meat is used, the fat content goes up. But this is such a lovely high-fibre, lower-fat version of a traditional South African dish, that we felt we had to include it.
● Because the lentils are well disguised in this dish, it is an ideal way to introduce reluctant legume eaters to this nutritious food.
● Apricot jam has a low GI as apricots have an extremely low GI and sugar has an intermediate GI. So, **diabetics,** add the jam for that extra flavour and be assured of good blood - glucose control.

TASTY PORK CASSEROLE
Serves 10

6 rashers salt-reduced lean bacon,
    cut into strips, all visible fat removed
2 onions, sliced
1 pkt mushroom soup powder
3 ml (½ t) white pepper
800 g pork fillet, diced
1 x 410 g tin small white beans, drained
250 ml (1 cup) white wine
250 ml (1 cup) water
250 g mushrooms, sliced (optional)

NUTRIENTS PER SERVING

Glycaemic index 42 ● Fat 9 g
Carbohydrate 9 g ● Fibre 2 g
Protein 22 g ● kJ 962

ONE SERVING is equivalent to 3 PROTEIN

1 'Fry' the bacon and onion in a little water until the onion is transparent and the bacon is crisp.
2 Mix a third of the soup powder and pepper and roll the pork pieces in the mixture. Add the pork pieces and beans to the onion and bacon. Heat and mix well.
3 Mix the rest of the mushroom soup powder with the white wine and water and pour the mixture over the beans and pork. Add the mushrooms. Turn the heat down and simmer for 40 minutes until the pork is done.
4 Serve on pasta or basmati rice, and with vegetables.

DIETICIAN'S NOTE:

● This is a delicious way to introduce the family to eating legumes in the form of beans. Because they are cooked in the mushroom sauce, they develop a delicious flavour, and add robustness to the sauce.
● No salt is needed in this recipe because of the soup powder.
● The only reason we can use the high-GI soup powder is because of the beans in the dish, which help to keep the GI down.
● Mushrooms are not suitable for those suffering from gout.

Bobotie, and Tasty pork casserole

ROAST LAMB AND BEANS

Serves 8. This is a very easy meal to prepare as it literally cooks itself. All the vegetables are roasted with the meat and only the gravy needs thickening just before serving.

1 x 410 g tin small white beans, drained
1 leg of lamb, deboned (± 1 kg)
10 ml (2 t) ground cumin
4 cloves of garlic cut into slivers, or
    10 ml (2 t) crushed garlic or
    10 ml (2 t) garlic flakes
500 ml (2 cups) peach juice
1 ml (¼ t) salt
freshly ground pepper to taste
3 small sweet potatoes
3 carrots, sliced
6 baby marrows, sliced
4 onions, quartered
60 ml (4 T) plain, low-fat yoghurt
15 ml (1 T) gravy powder or cornflour
parsley for garnishing

NUTRIENTS PER SERVING

Glycaemic index 43 ● Fat 8 g
Carbohydrate 34 g ● Fibre 6 g
Protein 32 g ● kJ 1506

ONE SERVING is equivalent to 3 PROTEIN, 1½ STARCH, 1 LIMITED VEGETABLE/FRUIT BUT remember, this is a WHOLE MEAL.

1 Preheat the oven to 160 °C.
2 Trim off as much of the outer layer of fat on the roast as possible. Rub the cumin into the meat.
3 Make little nicks in the surface of the meat and tuck in the garlic slivers.
4 Put the lamb into a large roasting pan with a lid or cover with aluminum foil.
5 Add the peach juice to the roast, season lightly with salt and pepper. Cover and roast for one hour, baste continuously.
6 Add sweet potatoes, carrots, baby marrows and onions and roast, covered, for another 30 minutes, baste occasionally.
7 Add the beans to the vegetables in the roasting pan. Cover and roast for 30–40 minutes.
8 To serve, remove the beans from the roasting pan and spread in a thick layer on a large platter. Arrange the vegetables on top of the beans.
9 Place the roast under the grill for about 5 minutes to brown, if necessary. Slice the meat and layer it on top of the vegetables.
10 Heat the cooking juices from the meat in a saucepan. Mix the yoghurt with the gravy powder and add to the sauce. Season to taste. Stir and cook until the sauce thickens.
11 Pour some sauce over the meat, beans and vegetables. Garnish with lots of parsley.
12 Serve with a mixed salad to complete the meal.

An unusual, yet delicious Sunday roast.
Roasting the beans in the meat gravy gives them a lovely rich flavour. Even the most ardent legume hater will have to admit that this way beans are quite acceptable.

DIETICIAN'S NOTE:

● As soon as red meat is used, the fat content is always higher. For this reason the meat portion is kept very small. This recipe, with only 8 g of fat per person, is a real bonus.
● In this dish, carrots are a minor component, and for this reason they can safely be included. Their high GI is offset by the beans and all the other vegetables.
● Leg of lamb has the lowest fat content of all lamb cuts.
● We usually do not advocate the use of gravy powder or cornflour, but in this case the low-GI beans compensate for the high-GI cornflour or gravy powder.
● This meal is exceptionally high in fibre.

MACARONI MINCE DISH

Serves 4

250 g (2½ cups) macaroni, uncooked
5 ml (1 t) canola or olive oil
1 onion, chopped
1 clove garlic, crushed
1 x 65 g tin tomato paste
200 g topside minced beef
3 ml (½ t) mixed dry herbs
30 ml (2 T) chopped parsley
50 g (4 heaped T) split lentils
200 ml (⅘ cup) stock (½ stock cube and
    200 ml water)
15 ml (1 T) Worcestershire sauce
salt and black pepper
5 ml (1 t) 'lite' margarine
25 ml (2 D) flour
2 ml (½ t) each; mustard and nutmeg
100 ml (⅖ cup) skim milk
100 ml cooking water from vegetables

extra tomato slices for garnishing
60 g low-fat Cheddar cheese
    (2 matchboxes)

1 Cook the macaroni in plenty of lightly salted water. Set aside.
2 Heat the oil and fry the onion for 1–2 minutes. Add the garlic and then the tomato paste and meat. Stir well and add the herbs, chopped parsley and split lentils.
3 Moisten the mixture with 200 ml stock. Add the Worcestershire sauce and season to taste. Simmer for 30 minutes.
4 For the white sauce, melt the margarine. Whisk in the flour, mustard, stock and milk, whisking all the time. Bring to the boil and simmer, stirring until the mixture thickens.
5 Remove from heat and mix the sauce with the macaroni.
6 Place ½ the macaroni mixture in an ovenproof dish. Spoon the meat over. Cover with the remainder of the macaroni and then the tomato slices. Sprinkle the grated cheese on top.
7 Bake for 30 minutes in a preheated oven at 180 °C.

DIETICIAN'S NOTE:

● Despite the fact that this recipe contains so little minced meat, it just makes the 10 g fat per portion aimed for. Using any red meat immediately increases the fat content considerably.
● Be sure to use LEAN topside mince, skim milk and low-fat cheese.

NUTRIENTS PER SERVING

Glycaemic index 30 ● Fat 10 g
Carbohydrate 60 g ● Fibre 6 g
Protein 28 g ● kJ 1868

ONE SERVING is equivalent to 3 STARCH and 3 PROTEIN

MEAT PIE

Serves 6. Very nutritious, and easy!

5 ml (1 t) canola or olive oil
1 medium onion, chopped
400 g topside mince
1x 410 g tin baked beans in tomato sauce
4 tomatoes, peeled and chopped
5–25 ml (1–5 t) chilli powder
1 ml (¼ t) salt
freshly ground black pepper to taste

PIE TOPPING:
1 x 410 g tin small white beans, drained
100 ml (⅖ cup) low-fat milk
1 egg

60 ml (4 T) water
250 ml (1 cup) cake flour, sifted
    before measuring
10 ml (2 t) baking powder
pinch of salt

1 Heat the oil and fry the onion until soft, add the meat and fry until brown. Add the beans, tomatoes and chilli. Season.
2 Simmer for 10–15 minutes. Add water if necessary.
3 For the topping, mash the beans together with the milk, water and egg, or process in a food processor or liquidizer.
4 Sieve the flour, baking powder and salt onto the beans. Mix well. Spoon the meat mixture into an ovenproof dish. Spread the topping over the meat.
5 Bake for 20–25 minutes in a preheated oven at 220 °C.
6 Serve hot with cooked vegetables or a large salad.

DIETICIAN'S NOTE:

● An unusual dish with a low fat and very high fibre content.
● Beans are legumes and contain both starch and protein. They can therefore be regarded as either starch, or protein, or half starch and half protein.

NUTRIENTS PER SERVING

Glycaemic index 48 ● Fat 9 g
Carbohydrate 40 g ● Fibre 11 g
Protein 25 g ● kJ 1495

ONE SERVING is equivalent to
2 STARCH and 3 PROTEIN or
3 STARCH and 2 PROTEIN
 (see DIETICIAN'S NOTE)

MOUSSAKA WITH SOUFFLÉ TOPPING

Serves 6

2 large brinjals, sliced (or 3 medium)
5 ml (1 t) canola or olive oil
1 large onion, chopped
5 ml (1 t) crushed garlic
½ green pepper, chopped
250 g topside mince
250 g (1 punnet) brown mushrooms, sliced
3 large tomatoes, peeled and chopped
10 ml (2 t) brown sugar
2 ml (½ t) cinnamon
2 ml (½ t) salt
100 ml (⅖ cup) fresh parsley, chopped
1 x 410 g tin mixed beans, drained

TOPPING
5 ml (1 t) 'lite' margarine
45 ml (3 T) flour
125 ml (½ cup) low-fat milk
250 ml (1 cup) cooking water from vegetables
2 egg whites
salt and freshly ground black pepper to taste
2 ml (½ t) nutmeg
180 ml (¾ cup) low-fat mozzarella cheese, grated (three matchboxes)

NUTRIENTS PER SERVING

Glycaemic index 30 ● Fat 10 g
Carbohydrate 25 g ● Fibre 10 g
Protein 21 g ● kJ 1250

ONE SERVING is equivalent to 1 STARCH and 3 PROTEIN

---

1 Place 30 ml water at a time in a large frying pan and steam the brinjal slices until cooked, but not too soft. Remove the brinjals and set aside.
2 Add oil to the pan and gently fry the onion, garlic and green pepper until the onion is transparent.
3 Add the minced meat and fry until browned.
4 Add the mushrooms and when soft, add the tomatoes, sugar, cinnamon, salt, parsley and beans. Cover and simmer for about 20 minutes.
5 For the topping, melt the margarine and stir in the flour, milk and half the vegetable stock with a whisk. Cook, stirring continuously, until thick and smooth. Add more vegetable stock if too thick. Do not overmix!
6 Beat the egg whites until stiff, and fold with the seasoning into the white sauce.
7 Alternate layers of brinjal slices and bean-mince mixture in an ovenproof dish, beginning and ending with a layer of brinjal.
8 Pour the topping over and sprinkle with the grated cheese.
9 Bake for 30 minutes at 180 °C. Turn off the oven and allow to stand in the oven for 15 minutes before serving.

Serve with basmati rice or durum wheat pasta, and a large salad.

DIETICIAN'S NOTE:

● For a vegetarian version, the minced meat may be left out altogether and another tin of beans used in its place.
● This moussaka is a very easy and tasty way to introduce legumes. The beans are part of the minced meat sauce and so are well disguised. Legumes have to be a PART of the meal, and not THE meal for those who are not used to them.
● Always use durum wheat pasta as it has a low GI. Home-made pasta made with flour has a high GI.

LIESBET'S CURRIED MINCE

Serves 6   Quick and easy for when you are in a hurry!

5 ml (1 t) canola or olive oil
1 onion, chopped
¼ green pepper, chopped
500 g topside mince
1 large brinjal, diced
2 ml (½ t) crushed garlic
5 ml (1 t) dried mixed herbs
2 ml (½ t) paprika
15 ml (1 T) vinegar
30 ml (2 T) red wine (optional)
15 ml (1 T) Worcestershire sauce
30 ml (2 T) tomato sauce, or
   'lite' tomato sauce
30 ml (2 T) braai sauce or BBQ sauce
5 ml (1 t) stock powder (¼ cube)
5 ml (1 t) curry powder
5 ml (1 t) turmeric

5 ml (1 t) masala
250 ml (1 cup) raw basmati rice,
   or 500 ml (2 cups) pasta or
   250 ml (1 cup) pearl barley

1   Heat the oil and gently fry the onion and green pepper until the onion is transparent. Add the meat, breaking it up while stirring and fry gently. Add the diced brinjal and fry lightly.
2   Add remaining ingredients, except rice, and mix well. Simmer on low heat until meat is done. Add water if necessary.
3   Cook the rice, pasta or pearl barley in lightly salted water.
4   Serve the curried mince on the pasta, pearl barley or basmati rice with a large tossed salad, or with two cooked vegetables, or sambals such as chopped onion and tomato; cucumber in plain, low-fat yoghurt; and green banana.

This mild curry dish is also suitable for children.
For a stronger curry, use 10 ml each of the curry powder and masala.

DIETICIAN'S NOTE:

● The nutritional analysis shown alongside is for the curried mince with basmati rice.
● With pasta the GI drops to 40, with pearl barley it drops to 18!
● Barley is high in soluble fibre which actively binds cholesterol and also helps with blood glucose control.

NUTRIENTS PER SERVING

Glycaemic index 48 ● Fat 8 g
Carbohydrate 22 g ● Fibre 2 g
Protein 20 g ● kJ 1071

ONE SERVING with starch is equivalent to 1 STARCH, 2 PROTEIN and 1 LIMITED VEGETABLE

MINI MEATBALLS

Makes 24 small meatballs or 6 hamburger patties

100 g (½ cup) red split lentils
400 g minced topside beef
1 medium onion, finely chopped
½ small green pepper, finely chopped
5 ml (1 t) crushed garlic
10 ml (2 t) dried mixed herbs
50 ml (4 D) tomato sauce, or
   'lite' tomato sauce
1 egg, lightly beaten
2 ml (½ t) salt
freshly ground black pepper
70 g (¾ cup) oat bran or oats

1 Cook the lentils in a saucepan of boiling water for 20 minutes or until soft. Drain well.
2 Preheat the oven to 200 °C while preparing the mince mix.
3 In a bowl, combine the lentils, beef, onion, green pepper, garlic, herbs, tomato sauce, egg, salt and pepper. Mix well. Add enough oat bran for a burger consistency. Shape into 24 small meatballs and place on a lightly greased baking tray.
4 Bake for about 40 minutes, or until cooked, turning halfway through the cooking time. Serve hot with two or three cooked vegetables or a large salad, and mustard or chutney if desired.

These meatballs make a great picnic snack if served cold, dipped into a sauce made of chutney and low-fat cottage cheese, or a dip made of 'lite' mayonnaise and chutney in a 1:1 ratio (remember to count 1 FAT).

DIETICIAN'S NOTE:

● Four mini meatballs would make up a portion containing 8 g fat, 20 g of protein and 1005 kJ per portion.
● If making **hamburgers**, ordinary bread rolls can be used as these patties have a very low GI. Together the roll and the patty would have a **GI of 57.**

NUTRIENTS PER MINI MEATBALL

Glycaemic index 33 ● Fat 2 g
Carbohydrate 4 g ● Fibre 1 g
Protein 5 g ● kJ 251

One MINI MEATBALL is equal to just under 1 PROTEIN
Four MINI MEATBALLS = 3 PROTEIN
One HAMBURGER PATTY = 3 PROTEIN
One HAMBURGER is equal to 2 STARCH and 3 PROTEIN

HERBED LAMB AND PASTA
Serves 4

250 g (3 cups) durum wheat pasta
tubes, e.g. penne, ziti
5 ml (1 t) canola or olive oil
250 g deboned lamb, any cut, all visible
fat removed, cut into 1 cm cubes
1 onion, chopped
1 stick celery, chopped
10 ml (2 t) crushed garlic
5 ml (1 t) dried tarragon
5 ml (1 t) dried rosemary, crumbled
½ chicken stock cube dissolved in
250 ml (1 cup) boiling water
1 x 410 g tin baked beans in
tomato sauce
60 ml (4 T) chopped parsley

NUTRIENTS PER SERVING
Glycaemic index 37 ● Fat 7 g
Carbohydrate 66 g ● Fibre 11 g
Protein 27 g ● kJ 1800

ONE SERVING is equivalent to 3 STARCH
and 3 PROTEIN

1 In a large pot of lightly salted boiling water, cook the pasta until just tender. Drain well.
2 Meanwhile, in a large non-stick frying pan, heat the oil until hot but not smoking over medium heat. Add the lamb and cook, stirring frequently, for 3 minutes until no longer pink.
3 Add the onion, celery, garlic, tarragon and rosemary, and cook for another 3 minutes, stirring gently.
4 Add the stock and beans and bring to the boil. Simmer for about 5 minutes, stirring frequently and mashing some of the beans against the side of the pan, until the sauce is slightly thickened.
5 Add the parsley, toss with the hot pasta and serve with a large salad

The mashed beans in this sauce add heartiness and thickens the sauce. The parsley adds a bright green note.

DIETICIAN'S NOTE:
● Mutton and lamb are the fattiest red meats available. It is for this reason that so little is used in this recipe, which together with beans help to bring the fat content of the dish down.
● This dish is suitable for **carbo-loading** as it is high in slow-release carbohydrates, and low enough in fat and protein.
● Pasta made from durum wheat (semolina) has a low GI. Home-made pasta made from flour has a high GI, as does commercial pasta made from soft wheat.

Herbed lamb and pasta

PASTA ALFREDO
Serves 4

250 g green flat ribbon noodles
5 ml (1 t) canola or olive oil
100 g smoked ham, finely slivered
½ chicken stock cube dissolved in
180 ml (¾ cup) boiling water
750 ml (3 cups) broccoli, chopped
60 ml (4 T) fresh basil leaves, chopped
freshly ground black pepper
250 g (1 tub) fat-free cottage cheese
60 ml (¼ cup) fat-reduced cream
15 ml (1 T) flour
250 ml (1 cup) cherry tomatoes, quartered

NUTRIENTS PER SERVING
Glycaemic index 33 ● Fat 7 g
Carbohydrate 51 g ● Fibre 5 g
Protein 22 g ● kJ 1489

ONE SERVING is equivalent to 3 STARCH
and 2 PROTEIN/DAIRY

1 Cook pasta in lightly salted water until just tender. Drain well.
2 In a large non-stick frying pan, heat the oil over medium heat until hot, but not smoking. Add the ham and cook for about 2 minutes, stirring occasionally, until lightly crisped.
3 Add the stock, broccoli, basil and pepper and bring to boil. Reduce the heat and simmer until the broccoli is cooked.
4 In a food processor, combine the cottage cheese, cream, and flour and process for 1 minute only, to a smooth purée. Add the cheese mixture to the pan, stirring until well combined.
5 Add the tomatoes and cook until the sauce is thickened and the tomatoes heated through.
6 Toss the sauce with the hot pasta, divide among 4 plates and serve with a salad.

Black forest ham, which is cured and smoked, has an intense flavour and texture and gives the best flavour. It is sold at most deli counters.

DIETICIAN'S NOTE:
● It is important to use fat-free cottage cheese and fat-reduced cream to keep the fat content low.
● Fat-reduced cream is available at Woolworths.
● This dish is suitable for **carbo-loading**, especially if double or 1½ times the pasta is used. The total carbohydrate per portion with 1½ times the pasta would then be 73 g carbohydrate.

PASTA WITH VEGETABLE RAGOUT
Serves 4

250 g (3 cups) shell noodles
5 ml (1 t) canola or olive oil
250 g lean bacon, all visible fat
    removed, diced
2 celery sticks, thinly sliced
2 carrots, thinly sliced
10 ml (2 t) crushed garlic
500 ml (2 cups) cabbage cut
    into 1 cm chunks
½ bunch spinach, chopped finely
1 x 410 g tin tomatoes, chopped
5 ml (1 t) dried oregano and marjoram
60 g mozzarella cheese, grated
    (2 matchboxes)

NUTRIENTS PER SERVING
Glycaemic index 33 ● Fat 10 g
Carbohydrate 56 g ● Fibre 8 g
Protein 21 g ● kJ 1667

ONE SERVING is equivalent to 3 STARCH
and 2½ PROTEIN

1 Cook the pasta in a large saucepan of lightly salted water until just tender. Drain well.
2 Meanwhile, in a large non-stick frying pan, heat the oil over medium heat until hot but not smoking. Add the bacon and cook, stirring frequently, until lightly crisped.
3 Add celery, carrots, and garlic and cook, stirring frequently, until the vegetables are cooked.
4 Add the cabbage and spinach and cook, stirring all the time until the cabbage is wilted.
5 Add the tomatoes with the juice, add the herbs, and cook, stirring until all the flavours are blended, for about 5 minutes.
6 Toss the sauce with the hot pasta, divide among four plates, sprinkle with the cheese and serve.

DIETICIAN'S NOTE:
● We suspect that spinach may have a high GI. For this reason, we recommend that it is only used in combination with other low-GI ingredients. The same applies to carrots.
● This dish is suitable for **carbo-loading** as is, or with extra pasta.

Pasta alfredo, and Pasta with vegetable ragout

PASTA WITH MINCE AND MUSHROOMS

Serves 4

250 g (3 cups) durum wheat pasta
  tubes, e.g. penne or macaroni
5 ml (1 t) canola or olive oil
1 onion, finely chopped
1 celery stick, chopped
125 g mushrooms, coarsely chopped
  (½ punnet)
10 ml (2 t) crushed garlic
300 g topside mince
60 ml (4 T) wine
½ beef stock cube dissolved in
  125 ml (½ cup) boiling water
½ x 410 g tin whole tomatoes, chopped
  with their juices
10 ml (2 t) sugar, optional
freshly ground black pepper to taste

1. Cook pasta in lightly salted water until just tender. Drain well.
2. Meanwhile, heat the oil in a large non-stick frying pan. Add the onion, celery, mushrooms and garlic and cook for about 10 minutes, stirring frequently, until the vegetables are soft.
3. Add the minced meat and cook until no longer pink. Add the wine, increase the heat and cook until almost evaporated.
4. Add the stock, tomatoes, sugar and pepper, cover and simmer for about 15 minutes until the sauce is rich and flavourful.
5. Divide the pasta among 4 bowls, spoon the sauce over, and serve.

This sauce freezes well. Freeze it in four individual portions and thaw in the microwave as needed.

DIETICIAN'S NOTE:
- As soon as red meat is used, the fat content of the meal automatically increases. Note that lean topside mince must be used, and how little is used.
- This meal is suitable for **carbo-loading** especially if the pasta is increased to 1½ times the amount. The carbohydrate per portion would then be 78 g carbohydrate.

NUTRIENTS PER SERVING
Glycaemic index 31 ● Fat 9 g
Carbohydrate 54 g ● Fibre 4 g
Protein 24 g ● kJ 1621

ONE SERVING is equivalent to 3 STARCH and 2½ PROTEIN

VEGETABLE AND BEEF STIR-FRY

Serves 6

250 g spaghetti, broken into 3–4 cm pieces
5 ml canola or olive oil
1 medium onion, chopped
15 ml grated fresh or minced ginger
1 clove garlic, crushed (5 ml minced garlic)
200 g minute steaks, cut into thin strips
1 stick celery, sliced
½ small yellow pepper, chopped
½ medium red pepper, chopped
200 g (2 cups) cauliflower florets
1 large carrot, cut into matchsticks
200 g (2 cups) broccoli, chopped
250 g (1 punnet) mushrooms, sliced
1 x 410g tin salad-cut asparagus,
  drained, water reserved
12.5 ml (1 D) soya sauce
20 ml (4 t) cornflour
200 ml (⅘ cup) water

1. Cook the spaghetti in a large saucepan of lightly salted water until just tender. Drain and keep warm.
2. Heat the oil in a wok or large non-stick frying pan. Add the onion, ginger, garlic and steak. Stir-fry over medium heat for about 3–5 minutes or until the steak is almost cooked. Add the remaining vegetables and stir-fry until just tender, sprinkling in a little water if necessary.
3. Mix the soya sauce, cornflour and the water from the tinned asparagus until smooth. Add the cornflour mixture to the stir-fry and stir until the mixture boils and thickens. Add the water as required if the sauce gets too thick. Add the spaghetti and stir until heated through. Serve immediately.

DIETICIAN'S NOTE:
- This is a wonderful, healthy, low-fat, low-GI meal, that is prepared within 30 minutes.
- Suitable for **carbo-loading**, especially if the spaghetti is doubled. (Carbohydrates are then pushed up to 68 g per portion).
- Asparagus is not recommended for those suffering from gout. Simply leave it out.
- Use soya sauce sparingly, as it is very high in sodium.

NUTRIENTS PER SERVING
Glycaemic index 33 ● Fat 4 g
Carbohydrate 38 g ● Fibre 6 g
Protein 18 g ● kJ 1079

ONE SERVING is equivalent to 1 STARCH, 2 PROTEIN and FREE VEGETABLES

Vegetable and beef stir-fry, and Pasta with mince and mushrooms

ROAST SWEET POTATOES OR BABY POTATOES

Serves 4

SWEET POTATO

BABY POTATO

2 small sweet potatoes or
16 baby/new potatoes
canola or olive oil

1 Cook the sweet potatoes or baby potatoes in their jackets in a microwave or on the stove in boiling water, until just done, but still firm.
2 Preheat the oven to 200 °C.
3 Peel and slice the sweet potatoes, but leave the skins on the new or baby potatoes. The potatoes may be cut in half.
4 Pour 25 ml oil (2 D) into a flat baking pan and place into the hot oven. As soon as the oil is hot, after about 5 minutes, remove the pan from the oven and pour ALL the oil out.
5 Place the cooked sweet potatoes or baby potatoes into the baking pan and toss or turn until completely covered in a thin layer of oil.
6 Roast, turning once, until evenly browned.

NUTRIENTS PER SERVING

SWEET POTATO
Glycaemic index 54 ● Fat 1.4 g
Carbohydrate 21 g ● Fibre 3 g
Protein 2 g ● kJ 480

ONE SERVING is equivalent to
1½ STARCH and minimal FAT

NUTRIENTS PER SERVING

BABY POTATOES
Glycaemic index 62 ● Fat 1.2 g
Carbohydrate 23 g ● Fibre 2 g
Protein 2 g ● kJ 497

ONE SERVING is equivalent to
1½ STARCH and minimal FAT

DIETICIAN'S NOTE:

● Potatoes have a high GI. But sweet potatoes and baby (new) potatoes with their skin have a lower GI. For this reason we have included a low-fat method of roasting sweet potatoes and baby potatoes to replace high-GI, high-fat roast potatoes.
● The sweet potato has more fibre and a lower GI than potatoes and is therefore more suitable for **diabetics.**

LEGAL CHEESE SAUCE FOR VEGETABLES

Serves 6

10 ml (2 t) 'lite' margarine
  (for flavour only)
150 ml (⅗ cup) low-fat milk *
150 ml (⅗ cup) water from boiling or
  microwaving vegetables **
1 ml (¼ t) salt
3 ml (½ t) mustard powder
50 ml (4 D) flour
60 g low-fat Cheddar cheese, grated
  (2 matchboxes)
3 ml (½ t) grated Parmesan cheese
  (optional)

1 Melt the margarine over low heat. Add the milk and vegetable water, then add the salt and mustard powder. Bring to the boil.
2 Meanwhile, mix the flour to a smooth paste with a little water.
3 As soon as the milk boils, pour a little hot milk onto the flour mixture and stir well. Pour the flour and water mixture back onto the rest of the boiled milk and vegetable water.
4 Return to the heat and boil until the sauce thickens.
5 Add the grated cheeses and pour over the cooked vegetables.

  * *Boxed long-life milk gives a creamier sauce without adding extra fat.*
 ** *Broccoli, cauliflower and courgettes (baby marrow) make the tastiest vegetable water for cheese sauce.*

NUTRIENTS PER SERVING

Glycaemic index 55 ● Fat 5 g
Carbohydrate 5 g ● Fibre negligible
Protein 4 g ● kJ 322

ONE SERVING is equivalent to ½ DAIRY
and ½ FAT

DIETICIAN'S NOTE:

● Parmesan cheese is high in fat but very strong in flavour. By adding just half a teaspoon to a dish with cheese, one is able to use less than half the amount of cheese – and half the fat – without sacrificing flavour.
● For a plain white sauce, omit the cheeses, add a dash of nutmeg and then count as ½ STARCH. This is also lower in fat.

YOGHURT FRUIT JELLY

Serves 6

1 x 410 g tin fruit cocktail in
    natural juice
1 x 85 g packet raspberry-flavoured jelly
    powder (sugar-free optional)
500 ml low-fat flavoured yoghurt

1. Drain the fruit cocktail and measure the juice. Add enough water to make 250 ml of liquid.
2. Bring the juice and water to the boil and then pour it over the jelly powder in a bowl. Stir until dissolved and cool but do not allow to set.
3. When the jelly just begins to set, fold the yoghurt and fruit through the jelly and mix well.
4. Pour the mixture into six serving bowls, cover and refrigerate until it has set.

NUTRIENTS PER SERVING

Glycaemic index 50 ● Fat 1 g
Carbohydrate 32 g ● Fibre 1 g
Protein 5 g ● kJ 641

ONE SERVING is equivalent to 1 STARCH,
½ DAIRY/PROTEIN and 1 FRUIT

DIETICIAN'S NOTE:

● In this case, normal jelly can safely be used as we know that sugar has an intermediate GI, and with the yoghurt the GI is lowered even further.

BAKED PEAR AND PASTA PUDDING

Serves 4

125 g (1 cup) durum wheat spaghetti,
    broken into 2 cm lengths
375 ml (1½ cups) low-fat milk
150 ml (⅗ cup) soft brown sugar
10 ml (2 t) 'lite' margarine
15 ml (1 T) grated lemon rind
30 ml (2 T) ground almonds
2 eggs, separated
6 tinned pear halves, in natural
    juice, drained

1. Preheat the oven to 190 °C.
2. Cook the spaghetti in plenty of lightly salted boiling water for 10 minutes, until just soft. Drain and place in a saucepan with the milk. Simmer for 20 minutes.
3. Remove the pan from the heat and let it cool.
4. Add the sugar and let it dissolve. Add the margarine, lemon rind, ground almonds and beaten egg yolks.
5. Whisk the egg whites until stiff peaks form and fold it into the pasta mixture. Pour half of this mixture into a greased ovenproof dish. Arrange the pear halves on top and cover with the rest of the pasta mixture.
6. Bake in the preheated oven for 30 minutes.

For a really different and delicious pudding, try this one. Once you get over the idea that pasta should not be in a sweet dish, you will love it.

NUTRIENTS PER SERVING

Glycaemic index 46 ● Fat 9 g
Carbohydrate 57 g ● Fibre 3 g
Protein 11 g ● kJ 1458

ONE SERVING is equivalent to 3 STARCH,
1 PROTEIN, 1 FRUIT, and ½ FAT

DIETICIAN'S NOTE:

● This is a good **carbo-loading** pudding. Low in fat, yet high in low-GI carbohydrates, and not too much protein.

Yoghurt fruit jelly, and Baked pear and pasta pudding

APPLE CRUMBLE
Serves 4

1 x 410 g tin pie apples
10 ml (2 t) lemon juice
30 ml (2 T) raw honey
50 ml (4 D) flour
250 ml (1 cup) oat bran
50 ml (4 D) 'lite' margarine
50 ml (4 D) soft brown sugar
1 ml (¼ t) salt

NUTRIENTS PER SERVING

Glycaemic index 56 ● Fat 8 g
Carbohydrate 46 g ● Fibre 4 g
Protein 3 g ● kJ 1156

ONE SERVING is equivalent to
2½ STARCH, 1 FRUIT and 1½ FAT

1 Place the pie apples in a greased pie dish, and pour the lemon juice and honey over.
2 Rub together the flour, oat bran, brown sugar, salt and margarine and sprinkle this mixture over the apples.
3 Bake in the oven at 180 °C until the crust is brown.
4 Serve with fat-reduced cream or custard made with low-fat milk, if desired (see recipe below).

DIETICIAN'S NOTE:

● The nutritional analysis is for the crumble on its own, without the low-fat custard or fat-reduced cream. With the custard the GI is lowered to 55.
● A good dessert for **carbo-loading**. High in carbohydrates and low enough in protein and fat.
● Although this dessert carries the orange Jack Spratt, the GI is just above 55.

LOW-FAT CUSTARD
Makes 4 x 125 ml (½ cup) servings or 8 x 62.5 ml servings (¼ cup)

500 ml (2 cups) low-fat milk or
  skim milk
30 ml (2 T) sugar
30 ml (2 T) custard powder
5 ml (1 t) vanilla essence (optional)

NUTRIENTS PER SERVING
(125 ml)

Glycaemic index 52 ● Fat 2 g
Carbohydrate 15 g ● Fibre 0.1 g
Protein 4 g ● kJ 417

ONE 125 ml (½ cup) PORTION is
equivalent to 1 STARCH and ½ DAIRY
ONE 62.5 ml (¼ cup) PORTION is
equivalent to 1 STARCH

1 Bring 400 ml of the milk to boil.
2 While the milk is heating up, place the reserved 100 ml of the milk and the sugar in a small bowl and mix to dissolve the sugar. Add the custard powder and stir to a smooth paste.
3 Just as the milk begins to bubble, pour half of it onto the custard powder mixture and stir. Pour this back into the hot milk and bring to the boil, stirring. Cook until thickened.
4 Add 5 ml vanilla essence, if desired.
5 Serve COLD with any one of the low-GI puddings.

To make banana custard, use half a banana per person with 125 ml (½ cup) COLD custard. The GI then rises by one point to 53.
Remember to count 1 FRUIT extra.

DIETICIAN'S NOTE:

● In the GI tables used in Australia, the GI of custard is given as 43. In South Africa we have not yet tested the GI of custard. The value we have given is the calculated value, based on the ingredients in this recipe.
● We feel quite sure that the true, tested GI of custard will be lower than the calculated value, due to the interaction of the nutrients with each other, especially when eaten cold.
● It is important to eat the custard COLD.
● When custard is hot, it has a higher GI value than when it is eaten cold. This is due to a change in the crystal structure of the cooked starch when it cools down. The starch in this case is the custard powder (*see* Factors influencing the GI, page 6.)
● **Diabetics** please note that if eaten cold, this low-fat custard is quite safe and will not suddenly raise your blood-glucose levels. It has a low GI despite the sugar in it!

Apple crumble, and Low-fat custard

CHERRY DELIGHT

Serves 12. A delicious pudding for that special dinner party.

1 x 410 g tin small white beans, drained
½ packet Boudoir biscuits
50 ml (⅕ cup) sherry (optional)
250 g (1 tub) low-fat cottage cheese
250 ml (1 cup) plain, low-fat yoghurt
1 packet vanilla instant pudding
1 x 410 g tin cherries in syrup
10 ml (2 t) gelatine

NUTRIENTS PER SERVING

Glycaemic index 51 ● Fat 4 g
Carbohydrate 27 g ● Fibre 3 g
Protein 8 g ● kJ 776

ONE SERVING is equivalent to
1½ STARCH and 1 DAIRY/PROTEIN

1 Mash the beans or process in a food processor until smooth, but not for longer than 3 minutes.
2 Arrange the biscuits in a single layer in an attractive glass serving dish and sprinkle the sherry over them.
3 Beat the beans, cottage cheese, yoghurt and instant pudding together with an electric beater or hand whisk.
4 Spread the mixture evenly over the biscuits and refrigerate until set.
5 Drain the cherries and cut in half. Arrange on top of the set cottage cheese filling.
6 Mix the gelatine into the cherry syrup and stir the mixture over low heat, until all the gelatine is dissolved. Cool.
7 When it is cool to the touch, pour the cooled cherry juice mixture over the pudding and refrigerate until set.

DIETICIAN'S NOTE:

● Although this recipe contains high-GI ingredients such as the Boudoir biscuits, the syrup from the cherries and the instant pudding powder, the beans, cottage cheese and the yoghurt offset these, and the end result is a low-GI pudding.
● This makes it a good choice of pudding for people with diabetes and hypoglycaemia, despite the sugar in it!
● Beating or processing ingredients for too long can raise the GI, therefore not more than 1–2 minutes should be spent on any single process, and the total time for beating, whisking, or processing in a recipe should not exceed 5 minutes.

BAKED WARM PUDDING

Serves 12

1 x 410 g tin small white beans, drained
2 eggs
75 ml (5 T) low-fat milk
30 ml (2 T) 'lite' margarine
100 ml (⅖ cup) brown sugar
180 ml (¾ cup) self-raising flour, sifted
   before measuring
1 ml (¼ t) ground cloves
1 ml (¼ t) ground cinnamon
10 ml (2 t) baking powder
180 ml (¾ cup) oat bran
15 ml (1 T) vinegar
60 ml (¼ cup) sultanas
2 ml (½ t) salt

NUTRIENTS PER SERVING

Glycaemic index 60 ● Fat 3 g
Carbohydrate 20 g ● Fibre 3 g
Protein 5 g ● kJ 548

ONE SERVING is equivalent to 1 STARCH,
1 FRUIT and ½ FAT

1 Preheat the oven to 180 °C.
2 Mash the drained beans with the eggs and milk, or process in a food processor, but not for longer than 1 minute.
3 Cream the margarine and sugar and add the beans. Mix well.
4 Sieve the flour, baking powder and spices together. Add the oat bran and lift a few times with the spoon to incorporate air.
5 Add the flour mixture to the bean mixture and stir well. Add the vinegar, sultanas and salt.
6 Spoon into a greased ring-cake pan and bake at 180 °C for 35–40 minutes.
7 Serve hot with cold Low-fat custard (page 108).

If preferred, low-fat evaporated milk can be used instead of custard. A lovely hot pudding for a cold winters night.

DIETICIAN'S NOTE:

● A double portion of this pudding with 125 ml custard would make a good **carbo-loading** pudding – 58 g carbohydrates per portion, with very little fat and not too much protein.

Baked warm pudding, and Cherry delight

APRICOT or PEACH CHEESECAKE
Serves 12. This is a really impressive dessert and very more-ish!

½ packet digestive biscuits
250 g low-fat cottage cheese
80 ml (⅓ cup) sugar
175 ml low-fat apricot yoghurt
2 eggs, separated
15 ml (1 T) gelatine
50 ml (⅕ cup) cold water
5 ml (1 t) vanilla essence
pinch of salt
2 x 410 g tins apricots or peaches
    in natural juice
20 ml (4 t) gelatine

NUTRIENTS PER SERVING
Glycaemic index 50 ● Fat 9 g
Carbohydrate 16 g ● Fibre 1 g
Protein 7 g ● kJ 696

ONE SERVING is equivalent to 1 STARCH
1 FRUIT and ½ DAIRY

1 Arrange the biscuits in a single layer in a 26 cm pie dish.
2 Using an electric beater, whisk the cottage cheese, sugar, yoghurt and egg yolks until smooth, but not for too long.
3 Soften 15 ml gelatine in the cold water and dissolve slowly over low heat. Slowly beat gelatine into cheese mixture. Add vanilla.
4 Whisk egg whites stiffly with the pinch of salt and then fold into the cottage cheese mixture. (Be sure to use clean beaters!)
5 Pour onto the biscuits and refrigerate for 2 hours until firm.
6 When the cheesecake is set, drain the fruit, reserving the juice in a saucepan (for the stove) or a glass jug (for the microwave). Heat the fruit juice and 20 ml gelatine until the gelatine is completely dissolved. Leave until cool to the touch.
7 Meanwhile, arrange the fruit on top of the cheesecake filling.
8 Spoon the cooled juice evenly over the fruit until all the fruit is just covered. Discard any excess juice and gelatine.
9 Return to the refrigerator until firm enough to slice.

DIETICIAN'S NOTE:
● Normally cheesecake is made with cream and high-fat pastry, which make for a very high-fat dessert.
● This recipe is as delicious as normal cheesecake, yet contains less than one third of the normal fat content. The bonus is that it also has a low GI.

 ## FRUIT SALAD
Serves 6

1 small papino, peeled and deseeded
1 small green apple
1 small red apple
3 oranges
1 banana
1 kiwi fruit
10 large grapes
10 ml (2 t) sugar (optional)

NUTRIENTS PER SERVING
Glycaemic index 47 ● Fat 0
Carbohydrate 23 g ● Fibre 4 g
Protein 1 g ● kJ 439

ONE SERVING is equivalent to 2 FRUIT

1 Cut the papino into cubes. Cut the apples into quarters (do not peel), remove the core and then chop into cubes.
2 Using a sharp knife, peel the oranges as you would an apple. Slide the blade of the knife between the segments and push the whole, peeled segments out into a bowl.
3 Peel and slice the banana.
4 Peel the kiwi fruit, cut in half lengthwise and slice thickly.
5 Cut each grape in half and remove the seeds.
6 Mix all the fruit together, add the sugar if desired and mix thoroughly. Chill before serving.

DIETICIAN'S NOTE:
● Adding lemon juice would lower the GI of the fruit salad.
● With the sugar, the GI of the whole fruit salad is 48. The reason for this is that the fruit has a lower GI than the sugar, so the sugar, with the higher GI, slightly increases the GI. But even at 48, the GI is quite acceptable.

GLYCAEMIC INDEX OF FRUITS
● **Tropical fruits** have higher GI values (*see* GI tables, pages 25–26).
● **Deciduous and citrus fruits** have lower GI values (*see* GI tables, page 25).
● The more tart (sour) a fruit, the lower its GI.

Fruit salad, and Peach cheesecake

BOSTON LOAF
Cuts into 14 slices

250 ml (1 cup) dried fruit cake mix
125 ml (½ cup) rooibos tea
250 ml (1 cup) oats
1 x 410 g tin small white beans
150 ml (⅗ cup) sugar
2 eggs, beaten
250 ml (1 cup) flour, sifted
10 ml (2 t) baking powder
1 ml salt
5 ml (1 t) lemon essence

NUTRIENTS PER SLICE

Glycaemic index 60 ● Fat 2 g
Carbohydrate 30 g ● Fibre 3 g
Protein 4 g ● kJ 673

ONE SLICE is equivalent to 2 STARCH

1 Pour the hot rooibos tea over the dried fruit cake mix. Add the oats, stir well and leave to soak for 10 minutes.
2 Meanwhile, process the drained beans in a food processor or liquidizer until smooth, but not for longer than 1–2 minutes.
3 Add sugar and eggs and process for 1 minute until combined.
4 Sift the flour and baking powder onto the fruit mixture and pour the bean mixture on top of this and then mix gently with a wooden spoon.
5 Add the salt and lemon essence and stir until combined.
6 Pour the mixture into a greased loaf pan and bake at 180 °C for 10 minutes. Turn the heat down to 150 °C and bake for 1 hour longer until pale brown and cooked through.

This makes a tasty, dense and heavy tea bread. Serve lightly spread with 'lite' margarine or eat as is.
If wrapped in tin foil, this cake will keep for two weeks. Perfect for taking on self-catering holidays.
Cakes made with beans need long, slow baking at a low temperature.

DIETICIAN'S NOTE:

● This teabread is suitable for **carbo-loading** as it is low in fat, and high in low-GI carbohydrates and not too high in protein. It should preferably be eaten as is, without any margarine.

CARROT CAKE
Serves 12

200 ml (180 g) 'lite' margarine
250 ml (1 cup) caster sugar
3 eggs (2 whole eggs + 1 egg white)
250 ml (1 cup) cake flour, sifted
    before measuring
pinch of salt
5 ml (1 t) bicarbonate of soda
10 ml (2 t) baking powder
7 ml (1½ t) ground cinnamon
2 ml (½ t) ground nutmeg
pinch of ground cloves
250 ml (1 cup) oat bran
125 ml (½ cup) grated carrot
    (1 large or 2 small carrots)
1 grated apple
150 ml (⅗ cup) sultanas

NUTRIENTS PER SLICE

Glycaemic index 61 ● Fat 10 g
Carbohydrate 37 g ● Fibre 2 g
Protein 7 g ● kJ 1102

ONE SERVING WITH ICING is equivalent to 2 STARCH, 1 FRUIT and 2 FAT

ICING
250 ml (1 tub) cottage cheese
60 ml (4 T) icing sugar
5 ml (1 t) vanilla essence

1 Cream margarine and sugar for not more than 3 minutes.
2 In a separate bowl, sift the flour, salt, bicarbonate, spices, and baking powder together. Add the oat bran, lifting the mixture with a spoon to incorporate air.
3 To the margarine and sugar, add eggs one by one, adding 2 or 3 tablespoons dry ingredients with each egg. Beat no more than 1 minute after each addition.
4 Stir the rest of the dry ingredients into the egg mixture using a wooden spoon. Fold in the raw carrots, apple and sultanas.
5 Place in a greased 25cm round cake tin and bake at 160 °C for 30–45 minutes. Leave to cool completely.
6 Mix ingredients for the icing. Spread over the top of the cake.

DIETICIAN'S NOTE:

● It is very important not to overmix this cake as this would make it more easily digestible and thereby raise the GI.
● The cottage cheese icing helps to lower the GI! Without it the GI would be 62 and the energy would drop slightly to 1039 kJ per portion.

Carrot cake, and Boston loaf

ORANGE AND SULTANA LOAF
Serves 12

1 unblemished orange, scrubbed clean
1 x 410 g tin small white beans, drained
200 ml (⅘ cup) sugar
20 ml (4 t) canola or olive oil
2 eggs, beaten
150 ml (⅗ cup) sultanas
5 ml (1 t) bicarbonate of soda
200 ml (⅘ cup) self-raising flour
60 ml (4 T) oat bran
150 ml (⅗ cup) Hi-Fibre Bran cereal
1 ml (¼ t) salt
5 ml (1 t) vanilla essence

ICING
50 ml (4 D) icing sugar
10 ml (2 t) lemon juice

NUTRIENTS PER SLICE

Glycaemic index 59 ● Fat 3 g
Carbohydrate 37 g ● Fibre 5 g
Protein 5 g ● kJ 817

ONE SLICE is equivalent to 2 STARCH,
1 FRUIT and ½ FAT

---

1 Preheat the oven to 180 °C.
2 Cut the unpeeled orange into quarters and remove any pips or blemishes. Place the orange quarters, skin and all, into a liquidizer or food processor and process for 30 seconds. Scrape down the sides and process for another 60 seconds until the orange is chopped up into small pieces.
3 Add the drained beans and process for another 30 seconds. Add the sugar.
4 Pour the orange mixture into a large mixing bowl and add the oil and eggs. Stir with a wooden spoon until well mixed.
5 Add the sultanas and mix.
6 Sift the bicarbonate and flour over the orange mixture, add the oat bran and the Hi-Fibre Bran cereal, and mix well with a wooden spoon. Add the salt and vanilla and stir well.
7 Spoon into a greased bread tin. Bake at 180 °C for 15 minutes. Turn the oven down to 150 °C, cover the top of the cake with foil, and bake for another 90 minutes. Cool completely.
8 For the icing, mix the icing sugar with the lemon juice, and drizzle over the top of the cooled cake.

This seems like a really odd mixture at first, but it makes the most delicious cake – crisp on the outside and moist on the inside.

DIETICIAN'S NOTE:

● A good **carbo-loading** cake. High in slowly absorbed carbohydrates, low in fat and protein.

 ## APRICOT TART
Serves 8

375 ml (1½ cups) oat bran
1 grated apple
75 ml (5 T) flour
2 ml (½ t) salt
125 ml (½ cup) sugar
50 ml (4 D) 'lite' margarine, melted
50 ml (⅕ cup) low-fat milk
1 egg, beaten
1 x 410 g tin apricots in natural juice, drained
10 ml (2 t) brown sugar

NUTRIENTS PER SLICE

Glycaemic index 55 ● Fat 6 g
Carbohydrate 33 g ● Fibre 3 g
Protein 4 g ● kJ 846

ONE SLICE is equivalent to 2 STARCH,
½ FRUIT and 1 FAT

---

1 Mix the oat bran, apple, flour, salt, sugar, then add the margarine, milk and egg.
2 Gently mix to a slightly sloppy batter.
3 Grease a pie dish, spoon in half the mixture and press down firmly.
4 Place apricots on top of the batter and then spoon the rest of the mixture on top of the apricots. Smooth over with a knife.
5 Sprinkle with 10 ml brown sugar.
6 Bake for 25–30 minutes at 200 °C until the top is brown and crisp. Allow to cool.
7 Cut into small wedges and serve with tea or coffee.

These are crispy topped wedges of tasty soft 'biscuit', made in the shape of a pie and cut up into small wedges.
This tart is best eaten fresh.

DIETICIAN'S NOTE:

● This is a delicious tea-time treat, but because oats are used instead of flour it is rather heavier than one would expect.

HEALTH RUSKS
Makes 60 rusks

250 ml (1 cup) oat bran
500 ml (2 cups) cake flour, sifted
25 ml (5 t) baking powder
5 ml (1 t) bicarbonate of soda
500 ml (2 cups) bran
500 ml (2 cups) Hi-Fibre Bran cereal
500 ml (2 cups) whole-wheat Pronutro
250 ml (1 cup) sugar
250 ml (1 cup) sultanas
2 apples, peeled and grated
250 ml (1 cup) 'lite' margarine
500 ml (2 cups) low-fat fruit yoghurt,
    any flavour (we used pear)
5 ml (1 t) salt
1 egg
5 ml (1 t) vanilla essence

1 In a large bowl, mix all the dry ingredients, except the sugar. Add the sultanas and the grated apple and with a wooden spoon lift up the mixture a few times to incorporate air.
2 Melt the margarine and sugar. Pour onto the dry ingredients.
3 Mix the yoghurt, salt, egg and vanilla. Add to dry ingredients.
4 With a wooden spoon, mix the yoghurt mixture into the dry ingredients until just blended. Add low-fat milk if too stiff. The dough should not be sloppy, but soft enough to spoon into pans.
5 Spoon into two sprayed bread pans and bake for 30 minutes at 180 °C. Turn down the heat to 150 °C and bake for 45 minutes.
6 Cut into 30 fingers per loaf and dry the rusks in a slow oven at 100 °C for 2–3 hours.

These are rather more-ish rusks despite them being so healthy.
This recipe can successfully be halved, should one wish to make a smaller batch of rusks.

NUTRIENTS PER RUSK

Glycaemic index 54 ● Fat 2 g
Carbohydrate 13 g ● Fibre 3 g
Protein 2 g ● kJ 349

ONE SERVING is equivalent to 1 STARCH

DIETICIAN'S NOTE:
● These rusks make a good **carbo-loading** snack.
● If raisins are used instead of sultanas, the GI is raised to 56, as the GI of raisins is substantially higher than that of sultanas.
● It is important to use fruit yoghurt, as the rusks will not be sweet enough if only plain, low-fat yoghurt is used.

APRICOT BISCUITS
Makes 40 bars or biscuits

150 ml (⅗ cup) 'lite' margarine
200 ml (⅘ cup) brown sugar
1 egg
5 ml (1 t) vanilla essence
500 ml (2 cups) flour, sifted before
    measuring
250 ml (1 cup) oat bran
5 ml (1 t) baking powder
pinch of salt
5 ml (1 t) cinnamon
150 ml (⅗ cup) apricot spread

1 Cream the margarine and sugar until light and fluffy, but not for more than 2–3 minutes.
2 Add the egg and vanilla essence and beat for 1 minute.
3 Sift the flour and baking powder and add to the mixture. Mix.
4 Add the oat bran, salt and cinnamon, and work to a soft, crumbly dough; add skim or low-fat milk, if necessary.
5 Press and pat half the mixture into a greased 30 cm x 20 cm swiss roll pan.
6 Spread evenly with apricot spread and grate the remainder of the dough on top.
7 Bake at 180 °C for 25–35 minutes.
8 When cool, cut into 40 bars, fingers or biscuits.

NUTRIENTS PER BISCUIT

Glycaemic index 57 ● Fat 2 g
Carbohydrate 12 g ● Fibre 0.5 g
Protein 1 g ● kJ 299

ONE BISCUIT is equivalent to ½ STARCH
and ½ FAT

DIETICIAN'S NOTE:
● Remember that beating a batter too long or vigorously can increase the GI.
● If diabetic (sugar-free) apricot spread is not available, ordinary apricot jam may be used. The GI will then be raised to 62.
● Omitting the jam or spread altogether **raises** the GI to 66!

APPLE AND SPICE BISCUITS

Makes 30 biscuits

250 ml (1 cup) oat bran
125 ml (½ cup) flour
125 ml (½ cup) whole-wheat Pronutro
5 ml (1 t) baking powder
125 ml (½ cup) Hi-Fibre Bran cereal
125 ml (½ cup) sugar
1 apple, grated
2 ml (½ t) ground cinnamon
1 ml (¼ t) ground cloves
50 ml (4 D) 'lite' margarine
1 egg, beaten

1 Mix all the dry ingredients with the grated apple and spices.
2 Rub the margarine into the mixed dry ingredients.
3 Stir in the egg, and mix to a stiff dough.
4 Using a teaspoon in each hand, place a heaped teaspoon of batter at a time on a lightly greased baking sheet and flatten to a round biscuit.
5 Bake at 180 °C for about 15 minutes or until lightly brown.
6 Carefully lift each biscuit off the baking sheet onto a cooling rack using an egg lifter. The biscuits are very soft as they come out of the oven, but become crisp on the outside as they cool.

This recipe makes for satisfyingly soft, chewy biscuits because of the apple in the dough.

DIETICIAN'S NOTE:
● These biscuits are particularly low in fat. Traditionally, biscuits have a high fat content, so this is a real bonus.

NUTRIENTS PER BISCUIT

Glycaemic index 56 ● Fat 1 g
Carbohydrate 8 g ● Fibre 1 g
Protein 1 g ● kJ 129

ONE BISCUIT is equivalent to ½ STARCH

ORANGE AND LEMON BISCUITS

Makes 30

125 ml (½ cup) flour
10 ml (2 t) baking powder
2 ml (½ t) ground nutmeg
125 ml (½ cup) whole-wheat Pronutro
375 ml (1½ cups) oat bran, pressed down
100 ml (6 T) 'lite' margarine
125 ml (½ cup) sugar
1 ml (¼ t) salt
1 egg
15 ml (1 T) grated orange rind (rind of one orange)
45–60 ml (3–4 T) lemon juice (juice of one lemon)

1 Sift flour, baking powder and nutmeg together; then add Pronutro and oat bran. Set aside.
2 Cream margarine, sugar and salt, add the egg and orange rind, and stir well.
3 Add the dry ingredients alternately with the lemon juice, and mix well. If too dry, add a little more lemon juice.
4 Drop teaspoonfuls onto a greased baking sheet.
5 Bake at 190 °C for 15–20 minutes, until the biscuits just start to go brown.

These tangy biscuits are almost like rock cakes.
Quick and easy to make.

DIETICIAN'S NOTE:
● Taking all the sugar out does not give the biscuits a low GI since the cake flour also has a high GI. Therefore, using sweetener does not really have an advantage.

NUTRIENTS PER BISCUIT

Glycaemic index 60 ● Fat 2 g
Carbohydrate 9 g ● Fibre 1 g
Protein 1 g ● kJ 259

ONE BISCUIT is equivalent to ½ STARCH and ½ FAT

INDEX OF RECIPES

ENDORSEMENTS

The following products used in the recipes in the book have been endorsed by the authors as low GI and low fat.

Jungle Oatbran
Lichtenblanc Low-fat Cheese
La Campania Low-fat Mozzarella Cheese
Bokomo Oats
Koo Beans
Kellogg's Hi-Fibre Bran

WOOLWORTHS:
Woolworths Chicken Breasts
Woolworths Minute Steaks
Woolworths Lean Topside Mince
Woolworths Low-fat Smoked Ham
Woolworths Frozen Hake Fillets
Woolworths Low-fat Milk
Woolworths 70% Fat-reduced Cream
Woolworths Olive Oil
Woolworths Tinned Chopped Tomatoes

Woolworths Small Pasta Shapes
Woolworths Spaghetti
Woolworths Macaroni
Woolworths Shell Noodles
Woolworths Fuselli Noodles
Woolworths Lasagne Sheets
Woolworths Fettuccini
Woolwoths Noodles
Woolworths Green Flat Ribbon Noodles
Woolworths Penne

CLOVER DANONE
Clover Danone Low-fat Plain Yoghurt
Clover Danone Smooth Yoghurt
Clover Danone Fruit Yoghurt

CLOVER
Clover Low-fat Smooth Cottage Cheese
Clover Low-fat Cottage Cheese
Clover Fat-free Cottage Cheese